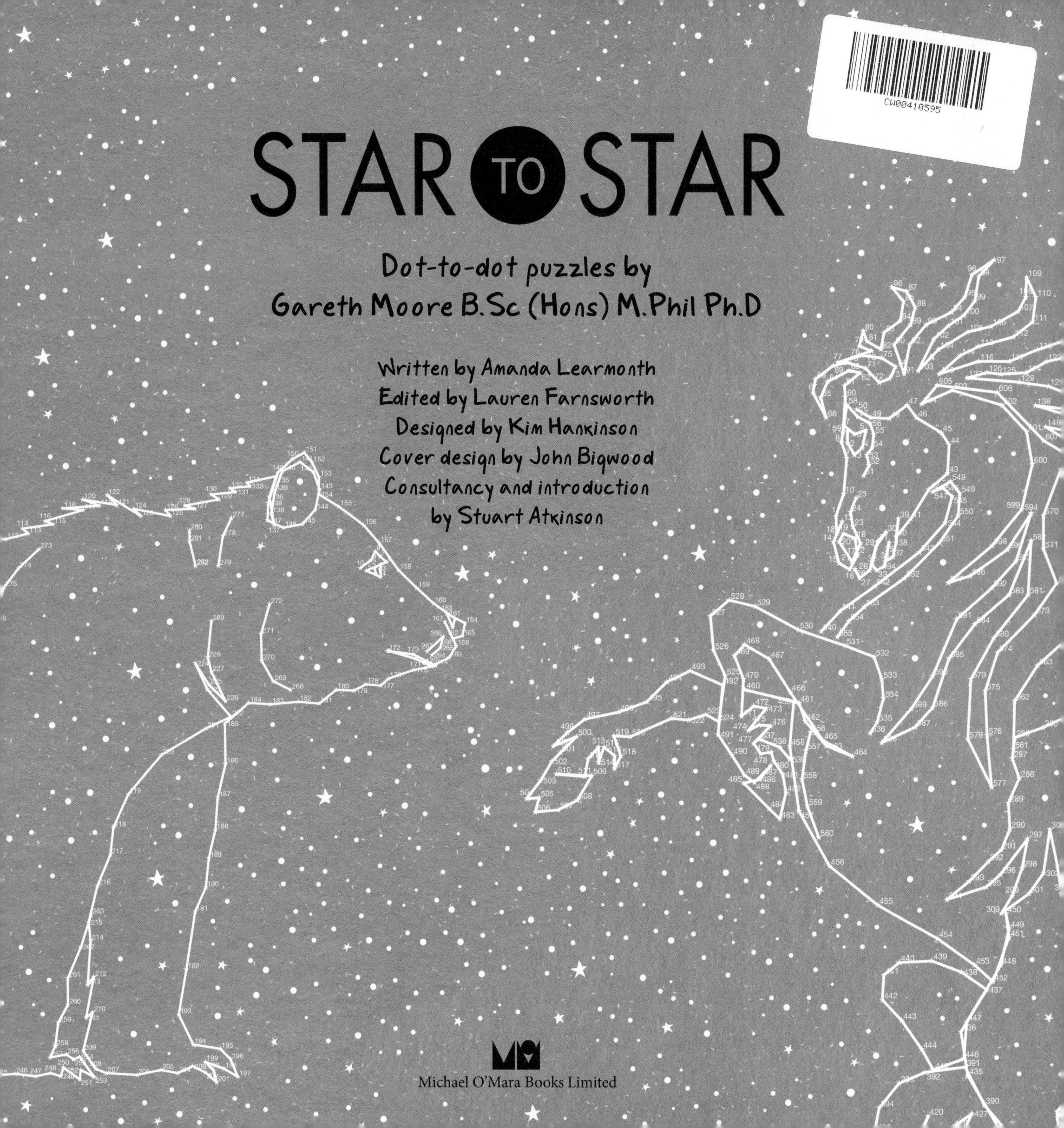

STAR TO STAR

Dot-to-dot puzzles by
Gareth Moore B.Sc (Hons) M.Phil Ph.D

Written by Amanda Learmonth
Edited by Lauren Farnsworth
Designed by Kim Hankinson
Cover design by John Bigwood
Consultancy and introduction
by Stuart Atkinson

Michael O'Mara Books Limited

CONTENTS

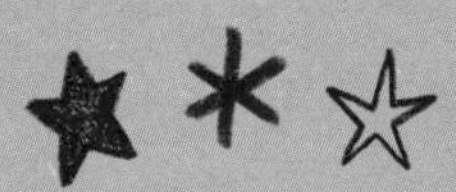

A GLANCE AT THE NIGHT SKY

For centuries, people have joined the stars in the night sky to make pictures and patterns called constellations. From Orion the hunter to Princess Andromeda and signs of the zodiac such as Leo and Cancer, these pictures have inspired storytellers and stargazers alike.

If you complete the puzzles in this book, joining star to star, you will reveal a cast of characters from myths and legends. Read their magical stories and find out fascinating facts about the celestial bodies that form each constellation.

Why not look out on a clear night and see which of the constellations you can find? You won't be able to see all of them from your window. Because the Earth is round, some can only be seen from the Northern Hemisphere† and some from the Southern Hemisphere.

AT THE BACK OF THE BOOK

Unfamiliar words are marked by a dagger symbol, like this †, the first time they appear and are explained in a glossary at the back of the book.

You'll also find a small, finished version of each image at the back if you need help with any of the puzzles.

HOW TO USE THIS BOOK

Start at number 1, which will always be a hollow star, and then draw a line to each numbered star in turn until you reach another hollow star.

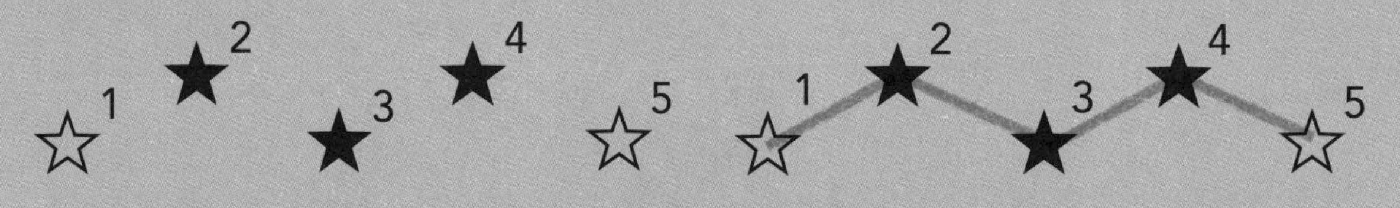

When you reach a hollow star, take your pen off the page and move to the next number, which will also have a hollow star. Then continue drawing a line from star to star.

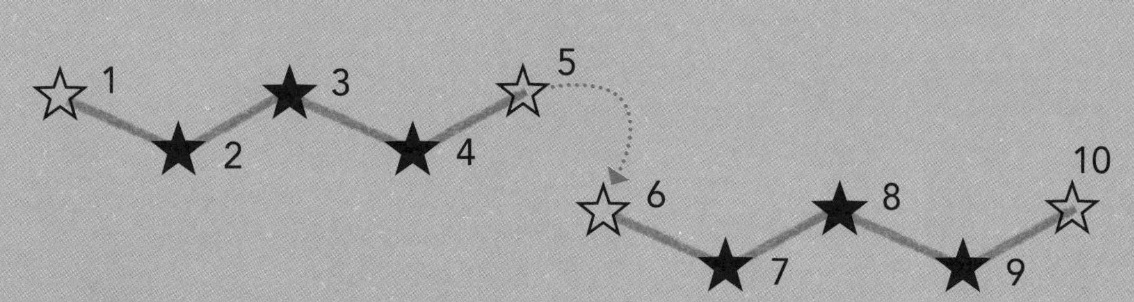

The final star of each puzzle will also be a hollow star with a bold number, so you will know when you have reached the end of the puzzle.

HINTS & TIPS

If you aren't immediately sure which star is attached to a number, look at the surrounding stars and numbers to work it out. Numbers are always directly above or to the side of a star, or at one of the four main diagonals to it. They are never at any other position, and are always exactly the same distance away from the star.

You don't have to start at number 1 – you can start anywhere you like and then fill in the bits you've missed out later.

Use a fine-tipped pen or pencil so that you don't obscure any stars and numbers you haven't yet used.

- Other than the constellation diagrams, the stars on each puzzle page do not represent actual stars in the night sky, and are for illustrative purposes only.
- The constellation diagrams are also positioned for design purposes only and do not represent the constellations' position or orientation in the night sky.

PISCES

Pisces is one of the largest constellations in the night sky and also one of the zodiacal constellations. Visible in both the Northern Hemisphere and Southern Hemisphere, this constellation has been recognized for over 3,000 years, although the ancient Babylonians associated it with a swallow bird.

PISCES AT A GLANCE

What does its name mean?
'The Fishes' in Latin

Which is the brightest star?
Kullat Nunu (Eta Piscium)

Where does this constellation lie?
In the Northern Hemisphere

To which constellation family does it belong?
The zodiac

* IN MYTHOLOGY

This constellation is based on a tale from Greek mythology, where the dragon-headed monster Typhon was attacking Mount Olympus. To escape, Aphrodite and her son Eros transformed themselves into fish and threw themselves into a river, first tying themselves together with rope so they wouldn't be separated.

* IN THE ZODIAC

Dates: 19th February – 20th March

Characteristics: compassionate and artistic

Zodiac symbol: ♓

KULLAT NUNU (ETA PISCIUM)

is the brightest star in the constellation. Also known by the name 'Alpherg', its radius is around 26 times greater than that of our Sun.

OMEGA PISCIUM

is a star around 100 light years† from Earth.

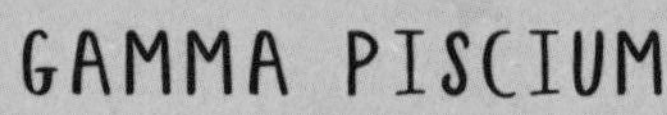

GAMMA PISCIUM

has about the same mass as our Sun, but is 10 times larger in radius.

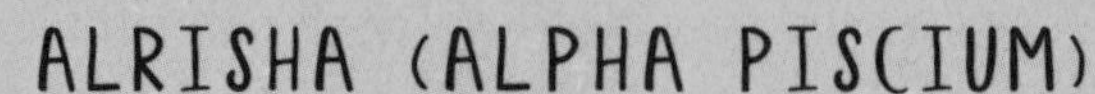

ALRISHA (ALPHA PISCIUM)

is actually two stars that orbit† each other. They are 18 billion kilometres apart and take around 700 years to orbit each other.

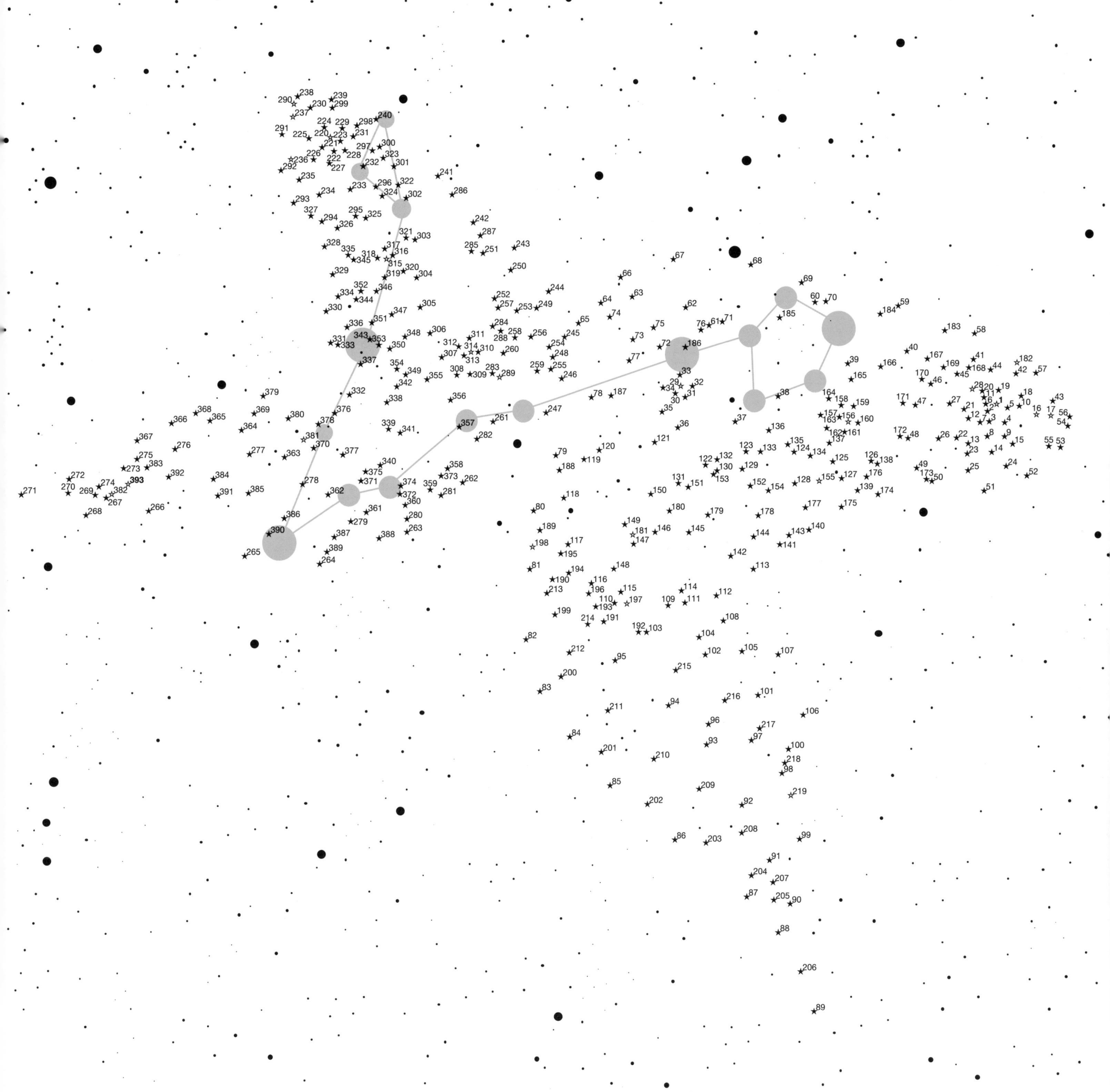

CAPRICORNUS

One of the zodiacal constellations, Capricornus means 'The Goat Horn' in Latin. It is located in the Southern Hemisphere and is one of the faintest constellations in the sky. It is associated with myths and images that go back to the 21st century BCE†.

✱ IN MYTHOLOGY

The story of Capricornus originated with the Babylonians and Sumerians, who knew it as 'the goat-fish'. In the early Bronze Age, Capricornus marked the winter solstice† and, in modern astrology, Capricorn's 'rule' still begins on the first day of winter. In Greek mythology, the constellation is associated with the forest deity Pan, who had the legs and horns of a goat. Pan was placed in the sky by Zeus, because he rescued the other gods in times of need.

✱ IN THE ZODIAC

Dates: 22nd December – 19th January

Characteristics: a love of family and tradition

Zodiac symbol: ♑

CAPRICORNUS AT A GLANCE

What does its name mean?
'The Goat Horn' in Latin

Which is the brightest star?
Scheddi (Delta Capricorni)

Where does this constellation lie?
In the Southern Hemisphere

To which constellation family does it belong?
The zodiac

ALGIEDI (ALPHA CAPRICORNI)
is approximately 690 light years away. Its Arabic name means 'the billy goat'.

SCHEDDI (DELTA CAPRICORNI)
is the brightest star in the constellation and rotates at an incredibly fast rate of 105 kilometres per second.

BETA CAPRICORNI
Its traditional name, Dabih, comes from the Arabic word meaning 'the butcher'.

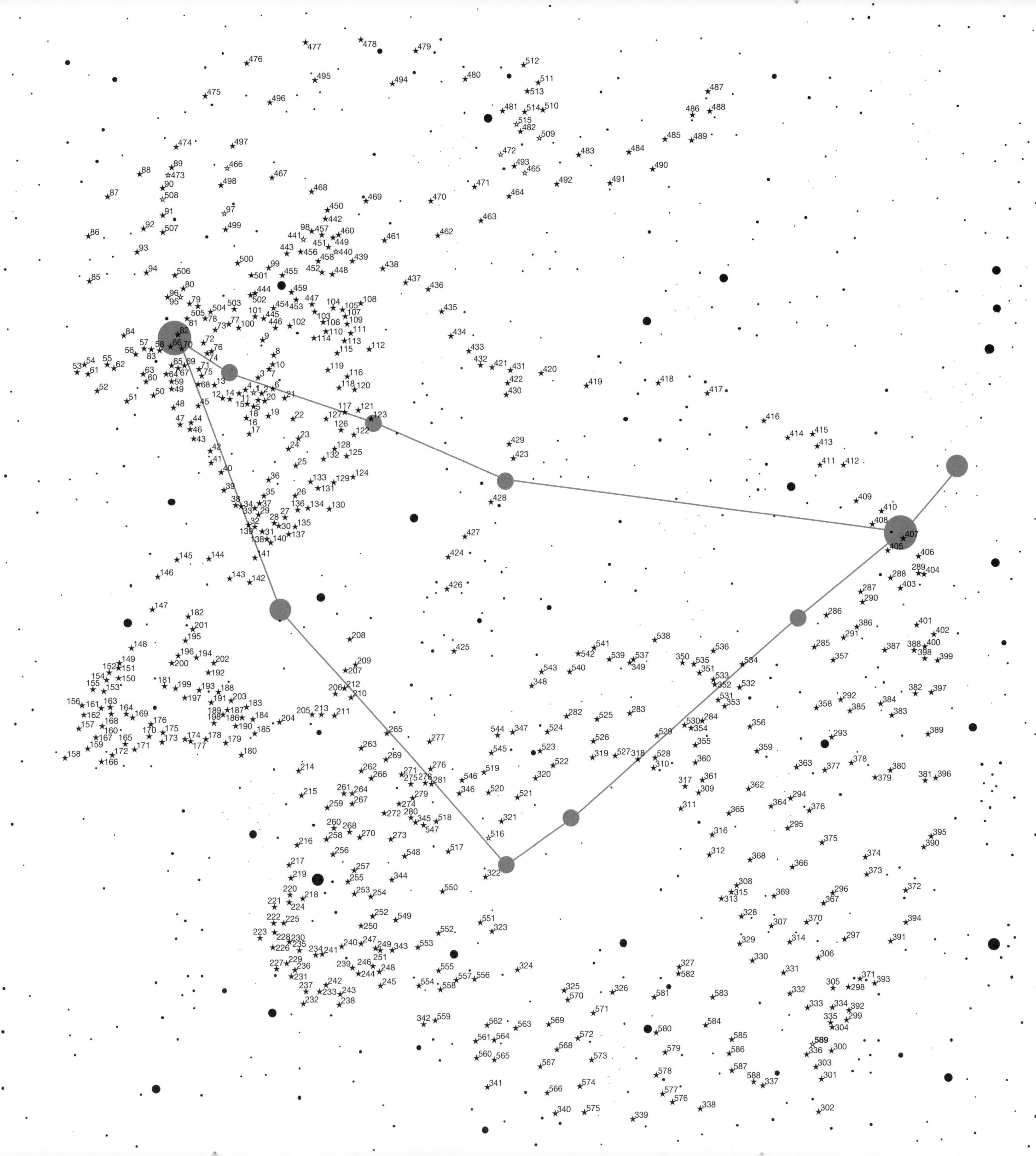

TAURUS

Taurus is one of the most prominent and visible constellations charging through the northern winter sky. It is also one of the oldest known constellations. Depictions of Taurus have been found in a cave painting dating back to 15,000 BCE.

TAURUS AT A GLANCE

What does its name mean?
'The Bull' in Latin

Which is the brightest star?
Aldebaran (Alpha Tauri)

Where does this constellation lie?
In the Northern Hemisphere

To which constellation family does it belong?
The zodiac

* IN MYTHOLOGY

In Greek mythology, Taurus is associated with Zeus who turned himself into a bull to kidnap Europa, the beautiful daughter of King Agenor. They had a son, Minos, who grew up to become the famous king of Crete who held the half-man, half-bull monster the Minotaur in a labyrinth.

* IN THE ZODIAC

Dates: 20th April – 20th May

Characteristics: a love of luxury and romance

Zodiac symbol: 

BETA TAURI is 700 times brighter than our Sun. Its traditional name, Elnath, comes from an Arabic word that means 'the butting', referring to the bull's horns.

THE PLEIADES or Seven Sisters is a star cluster. Its rising into the night sky often marked important calendar points for ancient peoples.

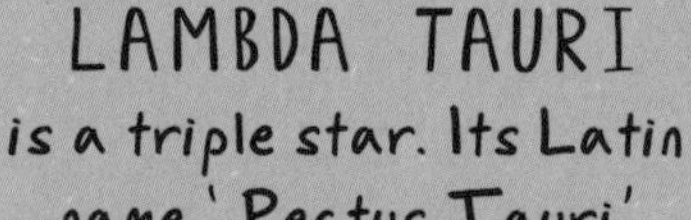

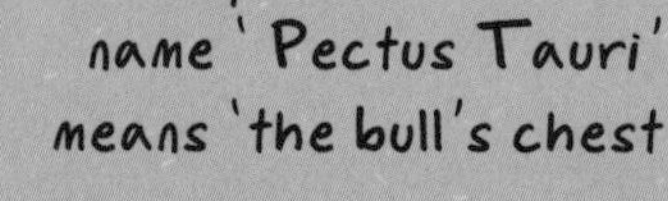

LAMBDA TAURI is a triple star. Its Latin name 'Pectus Tauri' means 'the bull's chest'.

ALDEBARAN (ALPHA TAURI) is an orange giant star. It is the brightest star in the constellation and the 14th brightest star in the sky.

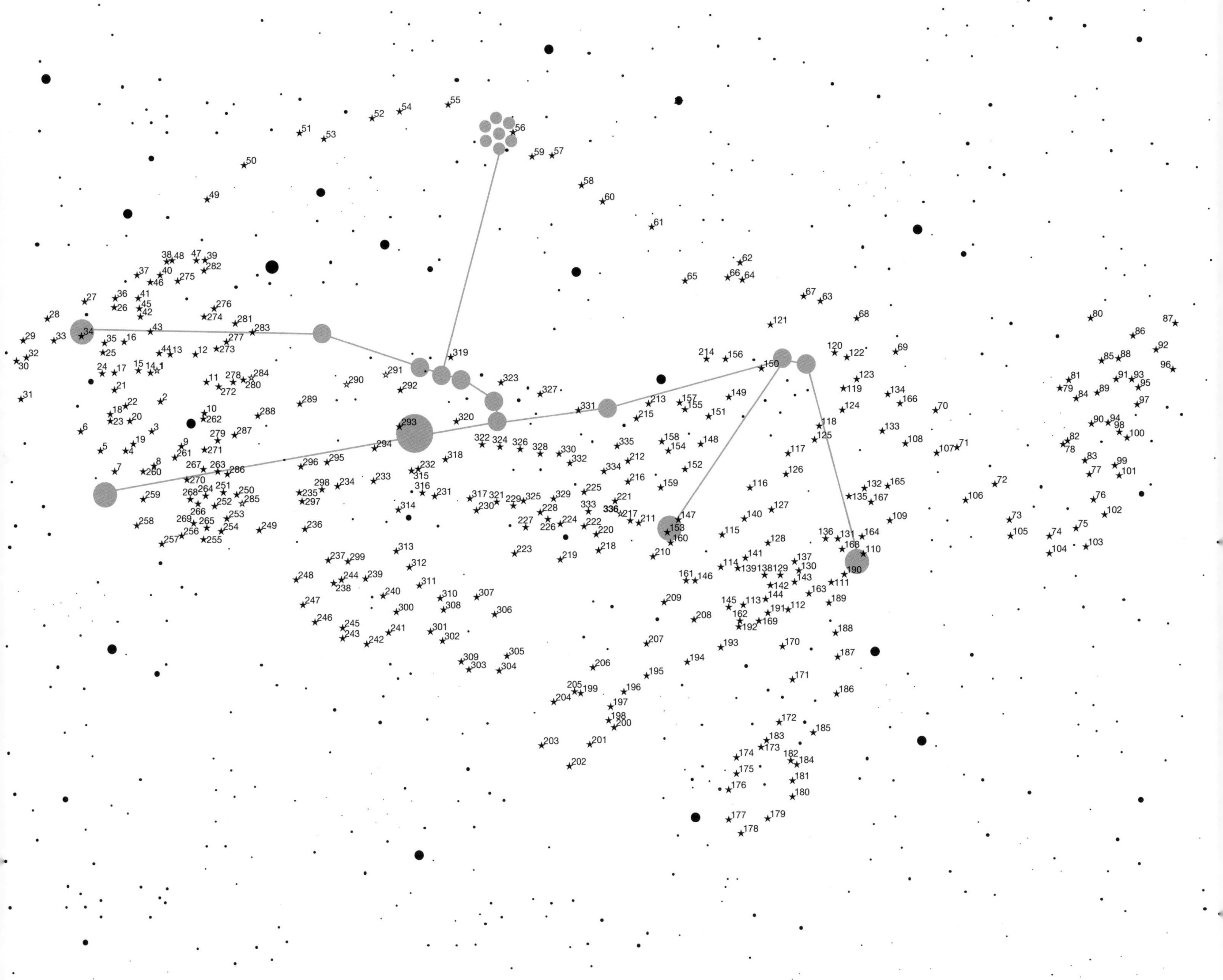

AQUARIUS

Aquarius is one of the oldest documented constellations of the zodiac. Its name means 'The Water-Bearer' (or 'The Cup-Bearer') in Latin. It lies in a region of the sky that is sometimes referred to as the Sea, because it contains a number of constellations associated with water, such as Pisces (The Fishes) and Cetus (The Whale).

AQUARIUS AT A GLANCE

What does its name mean?
'The Water-Bearer' in Latin

Which is the brightest star?
Sadalsuud (Beta Aquarii)

Where does this constellation lie?
In the Southern Hemisphere

To which constellation family does it belong?
The zodiac

* IN MYTHOLOGY

In Greek mythology, Aquarius is usually associated with Ganymede, a beautiful Trojan youth, who Zeus brought to Mount Olympus to serve as cup-bearer to the gods. In Egyptian tales, the constellation was said to represent the god of the Nile.

* IN THE ZODIAC

Dates: 20th January – 18th February

Characteristics: very independent and righteous

Zodiac symbol: ♒

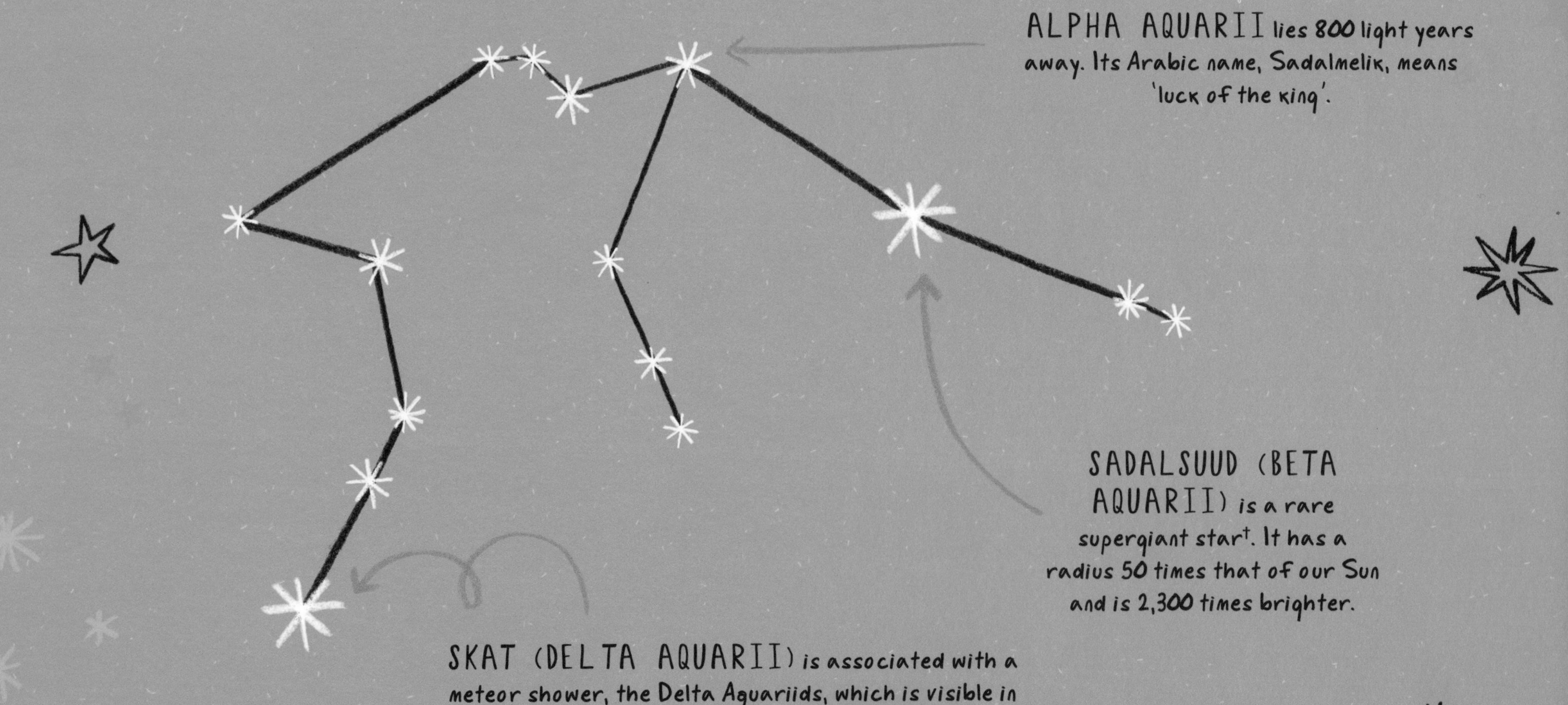

ALPHA AQUARII lies 800 light years away. Its Arabic name, Sadalmelik, means 'luck of the king'.
SADALSUUD (BETA AQUARII) is a rare supergiant star†. It has a radius 50 times that of our Sun and is 2,300 times brighter.
SKAT (DELTA AQUARII) is associated with a meteor shower, the Delta Aquariids, which is visible in both the Southern and Northern Hemispheres.

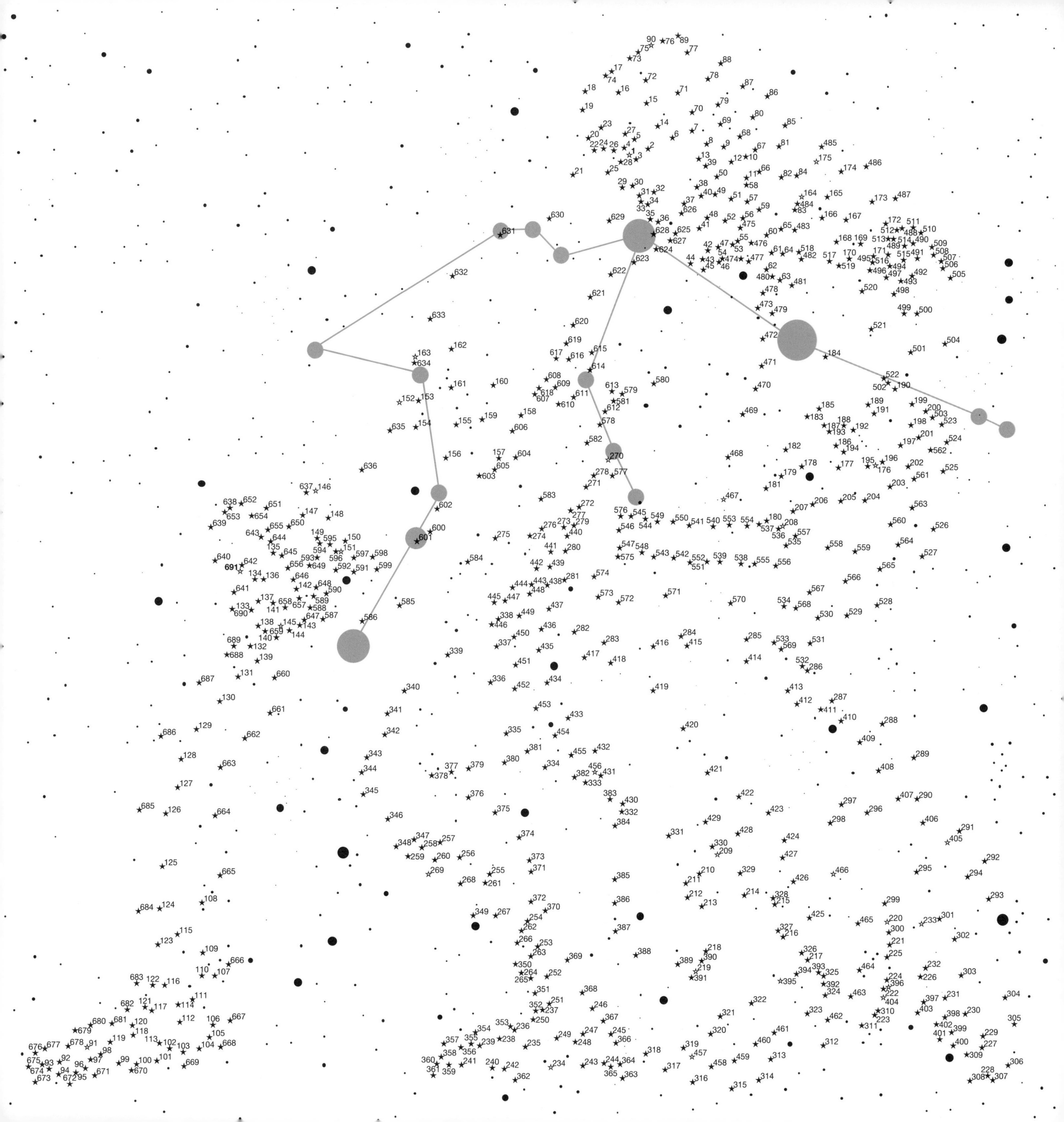

ARIES

The constellation of Aries is best viewed in the Northern Hemisphere in December. Like other zodiacal constellations, Aries, 'The Ram', was first catalogued by the Greek astronomer Ptolemy in the 2nd century.

ARIES AT A GLANCE

What does its name mean?
'The Ram' in Latin

Which is the brightest star?
Hamal (Alpha Arietis)

Where does this constellation lie?
In the Northern Hemisphere

To which constellation family does it belong?
The zodiac

* IN MYTHOLOGY

Aries is identified with the golden ram that rescued Phrixus, the son of a Boeotian king, from his evil stepmother. The ram was sent by his real mother, the cloud nymph Nephele. Phrixius sacrificed the ram to the gods and placed its fleece in a temple. This is the Golden Fleece, which later appears in the story of Jason and the Argonauts.

* IN THE ZODIAC

Dates: 21st March –19th April

Characteristics: courageous and determined

Zodiac symbol: ♈

HAMAL (ALPHA ARIETIS) is the brightest star in the constellation and the 48th brightest star in the sky.

BETA ARIETIS is 59.6 light years away. Its Arabic name, Sheratan, means 'the two signs'.

GAMMA ARIETIS is a triple star system. The meaning of its traditional name, Mesarthim, has been lost in history.

GEMINI

Gemini is easy to find in the night sky because of its two brightest stars, Castor and Pollux. Named after twin brothers from Greek mythology, these two stars mark the twins' heads, while fainter stars outline their bodies.

GEMINI AT A GLANCE

What does its name mean?
'The Twins' in Latin

Which is the brightest star?
Pollux

Where does this constellation lie?
In the Northern Hemisphere

To which constellation family does it belong?
The zodiac

* IN MYTHOLOGY

Castor and Pollux were the sons of Queen Leda of Sparta. They had different fathers, so they weren't true twins, but they were very close. Castor's father was Tyndarus, king of Sparta. Castor was mortal, while his brother Pollux, son of the god Zeus, was immortal. When they fought together in the Trojan War, Castor was killed. Distraught, Pollux asked Zeus to make Castor immortal, so the god placed both brothers in the sky to stand together forever.

* IN THE ZODIAC

Dates: 22nd May – 21st June

Characteristics: fun-loving, charming and chatty

Zodiac symbol: ♊

CASTOR is actually a complicated group of six stars, with three pairs of stars that orbit around each other.

POLLUX is the brightest star in Gemini and represents one of the twins' heads. It has at least one exoplanet†, called 'Thestias', orbiting it – a world more than twice the size of Jupiter.

MEKBUDA is a supergiant star, located on one of Pollux's legs. Its name is ancient Arabic for 'the lion's folded paw'.

STAR FACT

In mid-December star-gazers enjoy watching shooting stars zipping away from Gemini. During the Geminid meteor shower up to 50 meteors can be seen every hour.

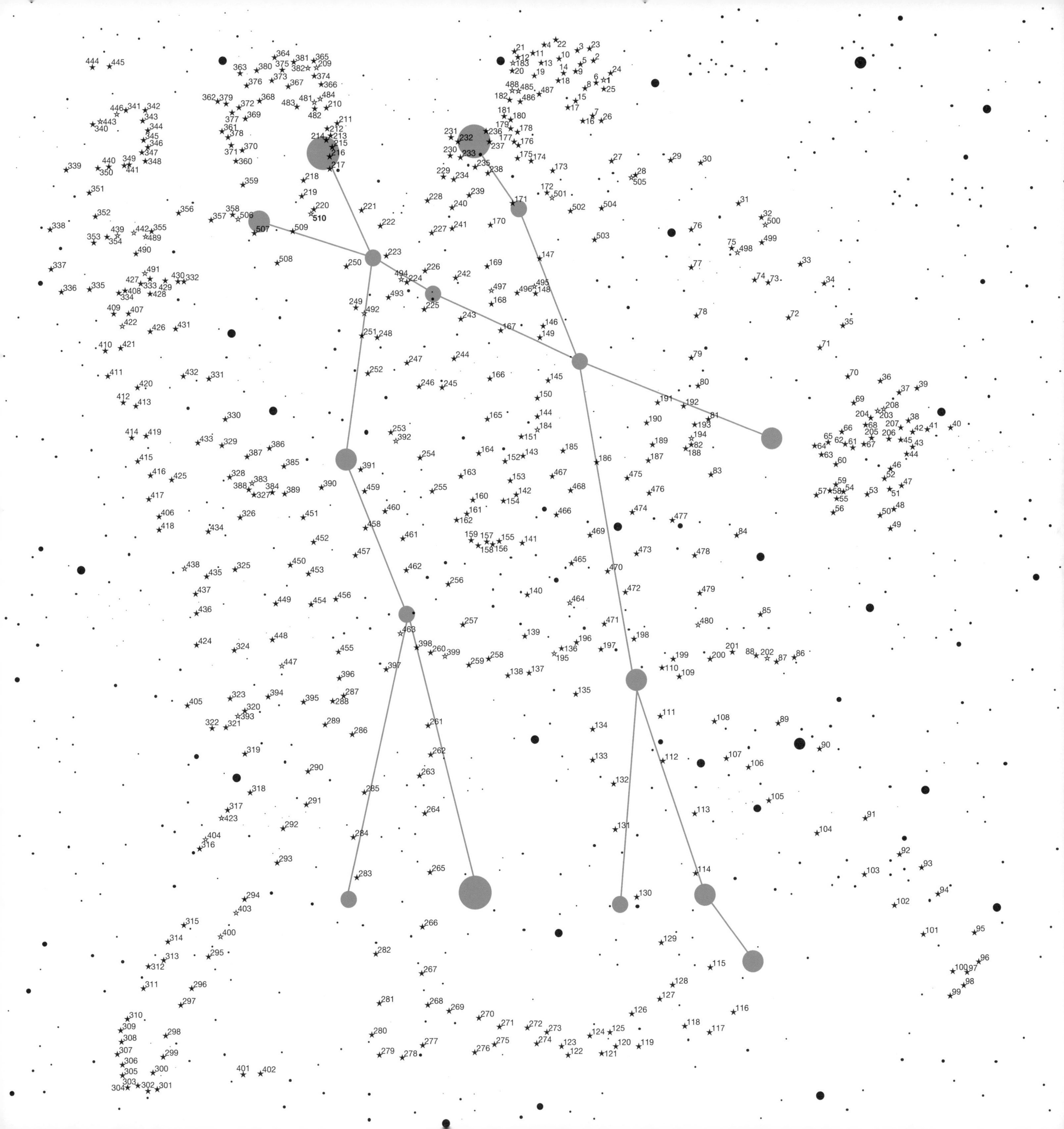

CANIS MAJOR

Canis Major, 'The Great Dog', can be seen faithfully following behind Orion. The constellation depicts the bigger of Orion's two hunting dogs (the other being Canis Minor, 'The Little Dog'). Canis Major is home to the brightest star in the night sky, Sirius.

CANIS MAJOR AT A GLANCE

What does its name mean?
'The Great Dog' in Latin

Which is the brightest star?
Sirius (Alpha Canis Majoris)

Where does this constellation lie?
In the Southern Hemisphere

To which constellation family does it belong?
Orion

* IN MYTHOLOGY

One Greek myth tells of Laelaps, a hunting dog that was so fast it could outrun all its prey. Laelaps was sent to hunt down the Teumessian fox, a giant fox so sly that no hunters could ever catch it. The chase between the two animals went on and on, until Zeus turned them both to stone, and placed Laelaps in the sky as Canis Major.

* AROUND THE WORLD

Other names for Sirius, Canis Major's brightest star, are:

- wolf (China)
- fox (Inuit regions of the Arctic)
- deer-slayer (India)
- Isis, Egyptian goddess and sister of Osiris (Egypt)

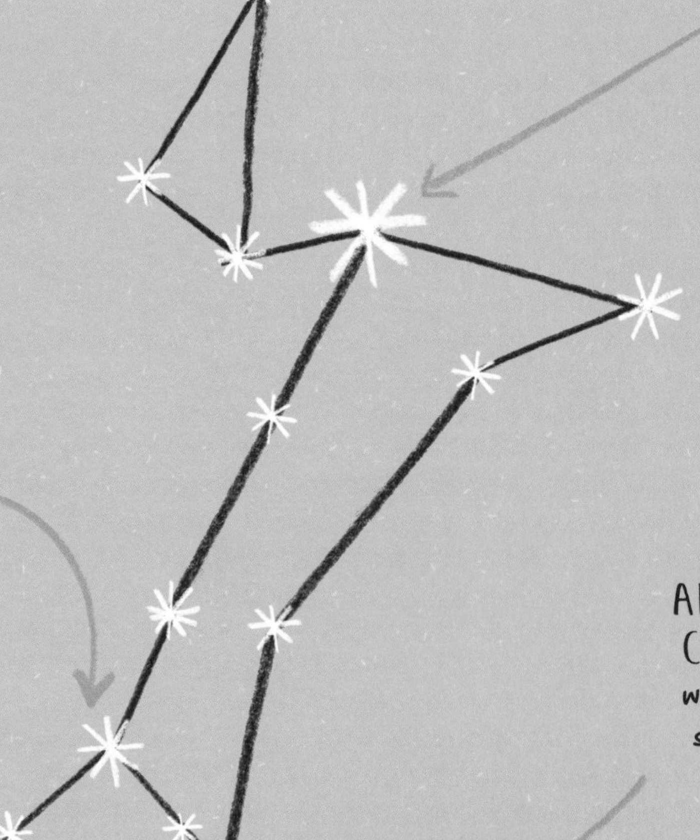

SIRIUS (ALPHA CANIS MAJORIS)
is also known as the Dog Star. It is 25 times brighter than our Sun, and is only 8.6 light years distant.

WEZEN (DELTA CANIS MAJORIS)
is a supergiant star. Its Arabic name means 'weight', which may be because it barely clears the horizon as seen from our latitudes†, as if something is weighing it down.

ADHARA (EPSILON CANIS MAJORIS)
was once the brightest star in the sky, about 4.7 million years ago.

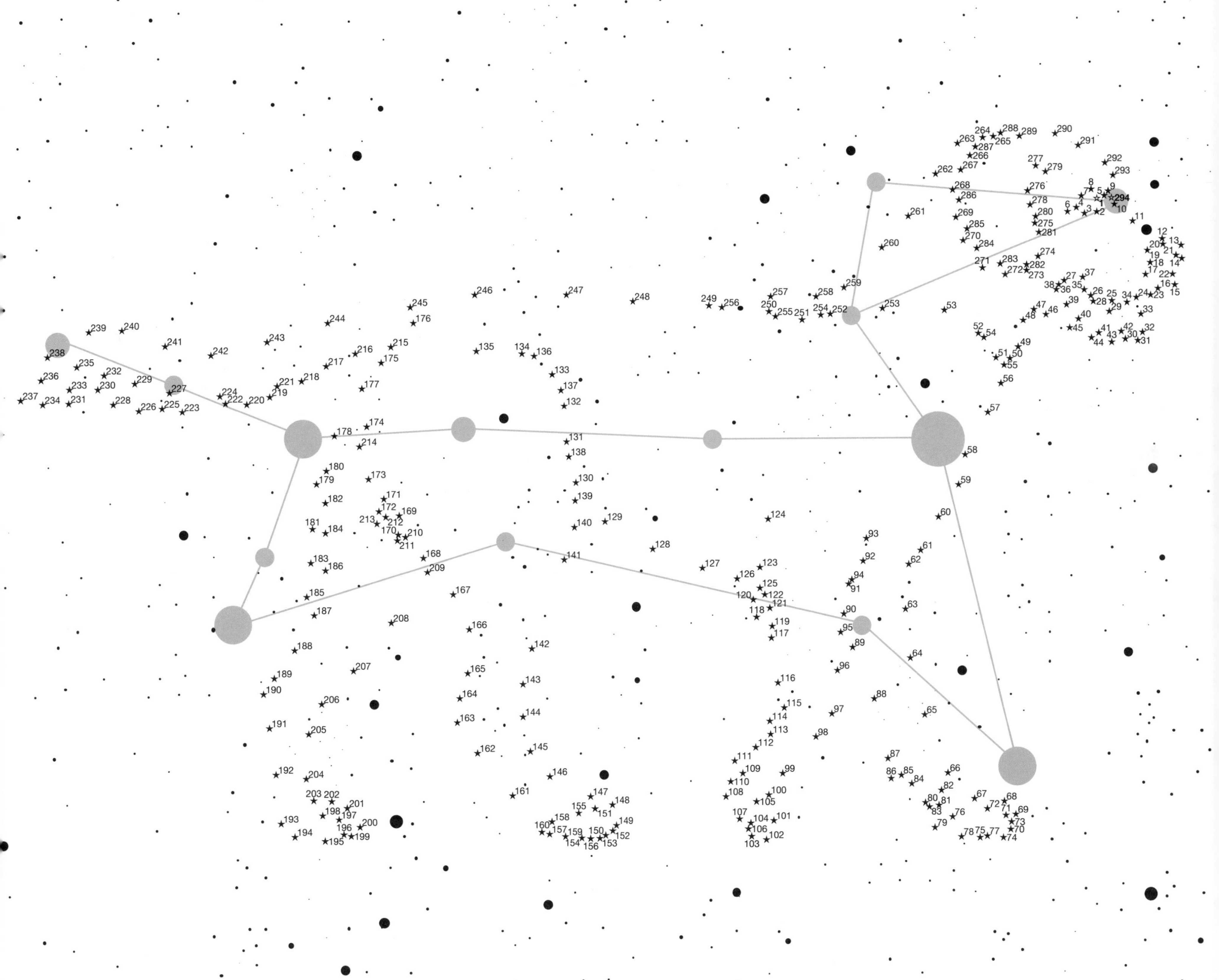

CORONA BOREALIS

Corona Borealis lies in the Northern Hemisphere. Seven bright stars form an arc that represents the crown of Ariadne, daughter of King Minos in Greek mythology.

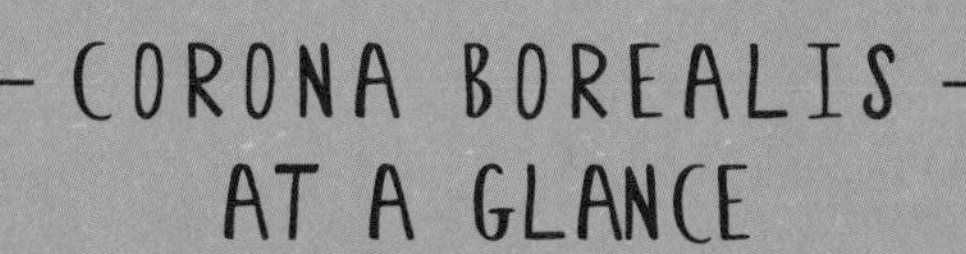

CORONA BOREALIS AT A GLANCE

What does its name mean?
'The Northern Crown' in Latin

Which is the brightest star?
Alphecca or Gemma
(Alpha Coronae Borealis)

Where does this constellation lie?
In the Northern Hemisphere

To which constellation family does it belong?
Ursa Major

* IN MYTHOLOGY

With Princess Ariadne of Crete's help, the hero Theseus escaped from the clutches of the Minotaur – the bull-like monster that lurked inside a vast labyrinth. Ariadne and Theseus fled together, but Theseus soon abandoned the princess. Finding Ariadne alone and weeping, the god Dionysus fell in love with her and they were married. Ariadne wore a beautiful jewelled crown at her wedding. She threw the crown into the sky, where it remained as the constellation Corona Borealis.

* AROUND THE WORLD

Corona Borealis has also been depicted as:

- a broken dish (Arab)
- a boomerang (Aboriginal Australia)
- a polar bear's paw (Siberia)
- the castle of the goddess Lady Arianrhod (Wales)

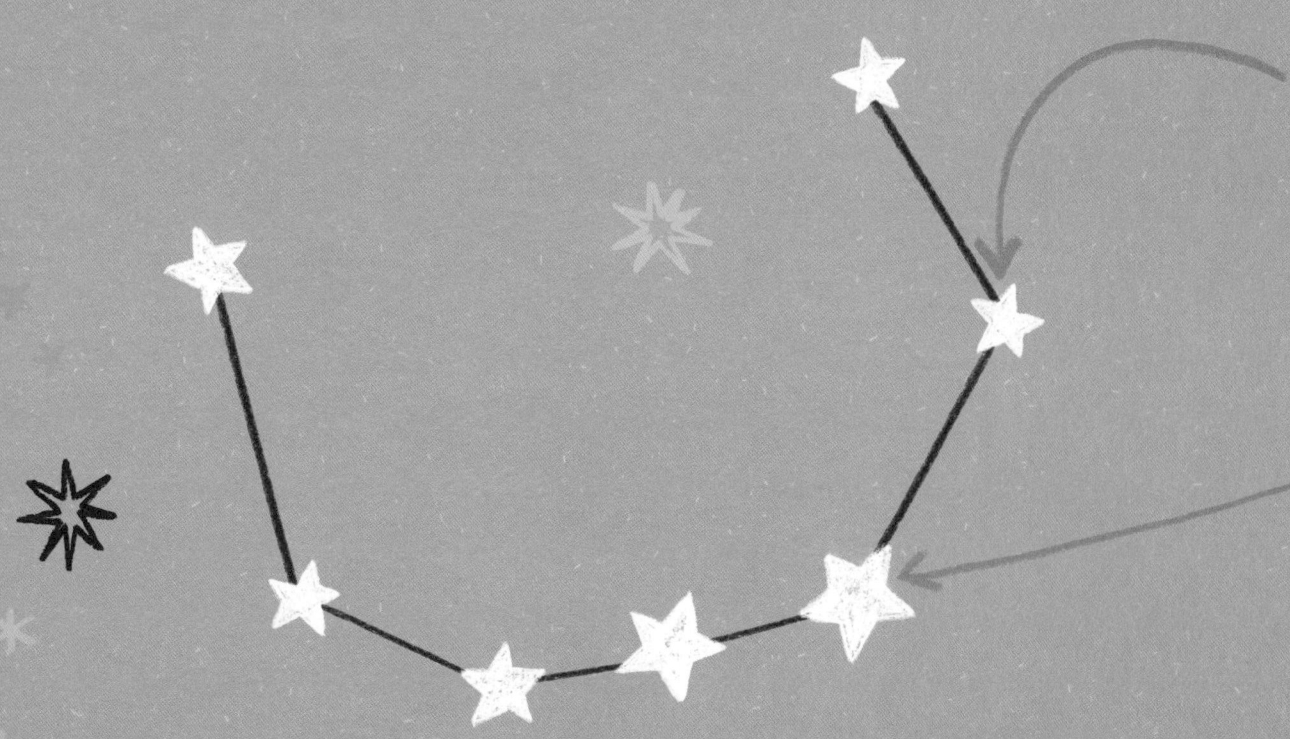

NUSAKAN (BETA CORONAE BOREALIS) is a binary star† and is the second brightest in the constellation.

ALPHECCA (ALPHA CORONAE BOREALIS) is the brightest star in Ariadne's crown. Its Latin name is 'Gemma', which means 'jewel'.

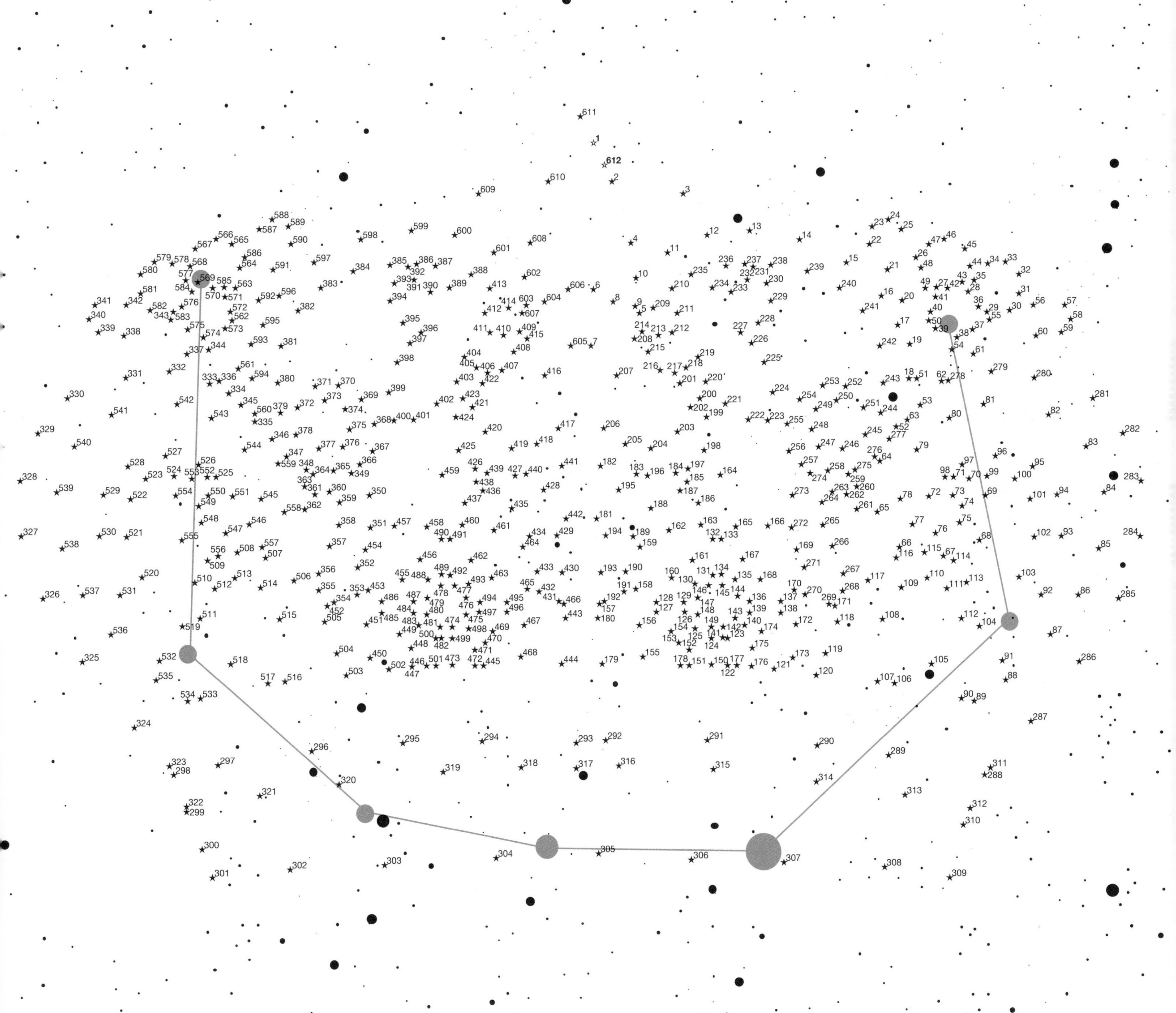

CANCER

Even on a moonless night, you may struggle to make out the zodiac's faintest constellation, Cancer. It appears like an upside-down 'Y' with a misty patch in the middle. This patch is 'The Beehive' star cluster, so named because it looks like a swarm of bees in the sky.

CANCER AT A GLANCE

What does its name mean?
'The Crab' in Latin

Which is the brightest star?
Al Tarf (Beta Cancri)

Where does this constellation lie?
In the Northern Hemisphere

To which constellation family does it belong?
The zodiac

* IN MYTHOLOGY

A widely known Greek myth associates Cancer with a giant crab. The crab was sent by jealous goddess named Hera to distract Heracles (Hercules in Roman myth) while he was fighting the hideous, multi-headed beast Hydra. The crab bit Heracles, but the mighty hero crushed it with one blow. To reward its efforts, Hera placed the crab in the sky. But because the creature did not accomplish its mission, it only dwells among the dimmest stars.

* IN THE ZODIAC

Dates: 22nd June – 22nd July

Characteristics: prone to mood swings, but also very loyal and loving

Zodiac symbol: ♋

ASELLUS BOREALIS (GAMMA CANCRI)

means 'northern donkey colt', based on a Greek myth in which the gods rode on donkeys into battle against the Giants. The Giants thought the donkeys were monsters and fled.

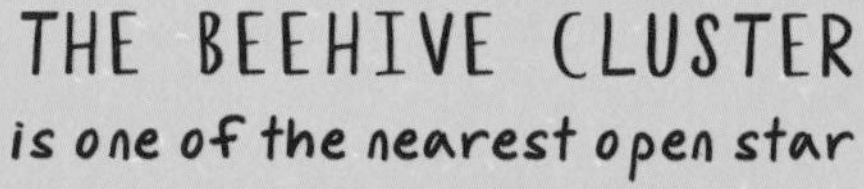

THE BEEHIVE CLUSTER

is one of the nearest open star clusters† to our Solar System.

ASELLUS AUSTRALIS (DELTA CANCRI)

means 'southern donkey colt' in Latin. This star also holds the record for the longest alternative name – Arkushanangarushashutu – Babylonian for 'the southeast star in the crab'.

AL TARF (BETA CANCRI)

is the brightest star in the Cancer constellation. Its name derives from the Arabic for 'eye' or 'the glance' (of Leo).

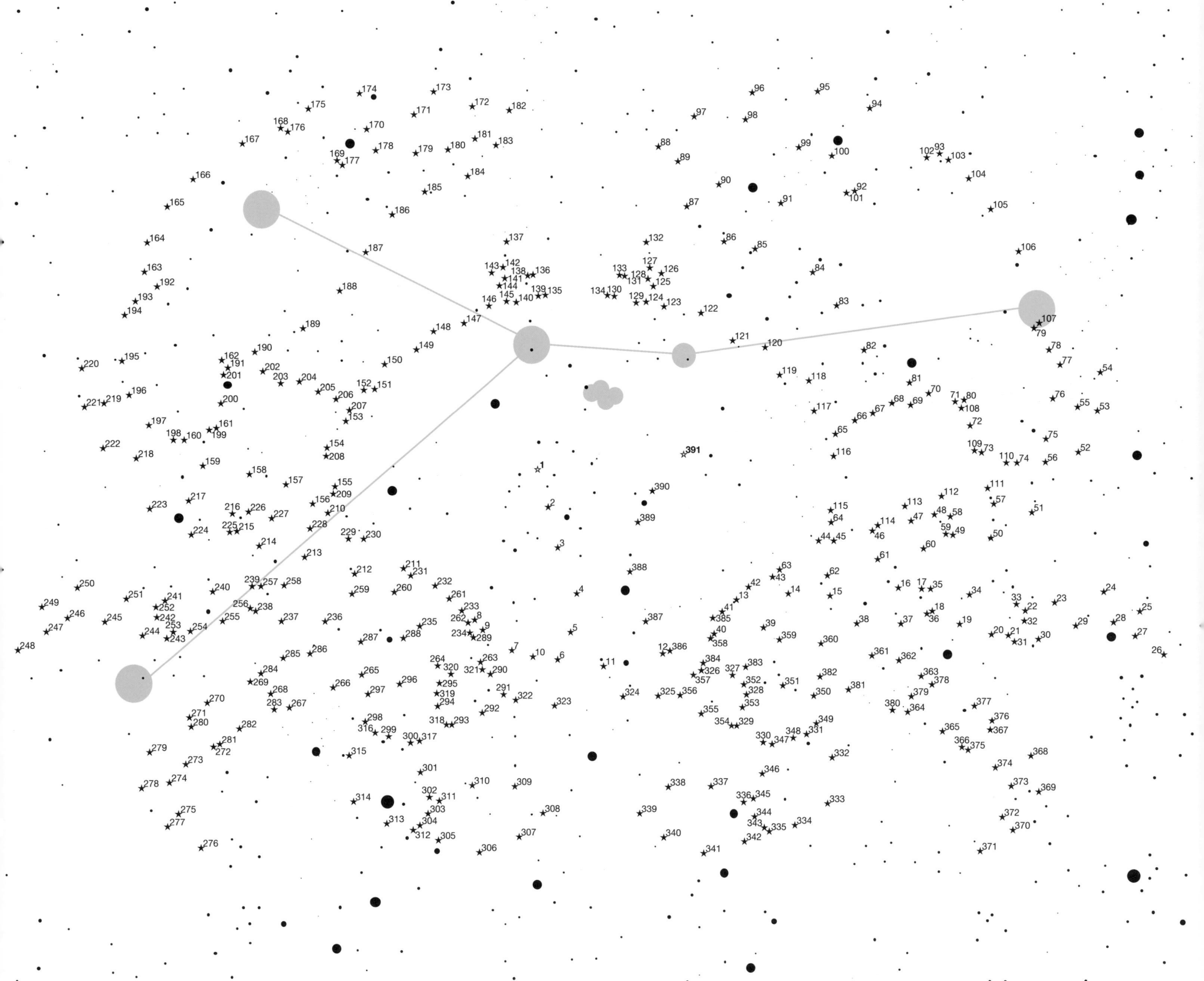

LEO

With its distinctive pattern of a crouching lion and many bright stars, Leo, 'The Lion', is one of the easiest zodiacal constellations to spot. It is also one of the oldest known – the Mesopotamians recognized a lion shape as early as 4000 BCE.

LEO AT A GLANCE

What does its name mean?
'The Lion' in Latin

Which is the brightest star?
Regulus (Alpha Leonis)

Where does this constellation lie?
In the Northern Hemisphere

To which constellation family does it belong?
The zodiac

IN MYTHOLOGY

As part of his 12 labours, the hero Heracles (Hercules in Roman myth) was tasked with killing a huge, powerful lion, known as the Nemean lion. The lion possessed a super-strong hide that couldn't be punctured by any weapon, so Heracles wrestled the beast with his bare hands and strangled it to death. The lion was then placed in the sky as the constellation of Leo.

IN THE ZODIAC

Dates: 23rd July – 22nd August

Characteristics: creative and cheerful, but with a tendency to be stubborn and lazy

Zodiac symbol: ♌

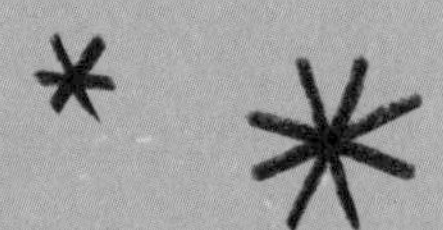

THE SICKLE is an asterism† that forms a shape like a sickle (a tool with a curved blade).

ALGEIBA is a binary star and one of the six other bright stars of Leo that represent the lion's head. In Arabic, this star means 'the lion's mane'.

DENEBOLA (BETA LEONIS) is the third brightest star in the constellation, marking the lion's tail.

REGULUS (ALPHA LEONIS) is Leo's brightest star and means 'little king' in Latin. Its position marks the lion's heart.

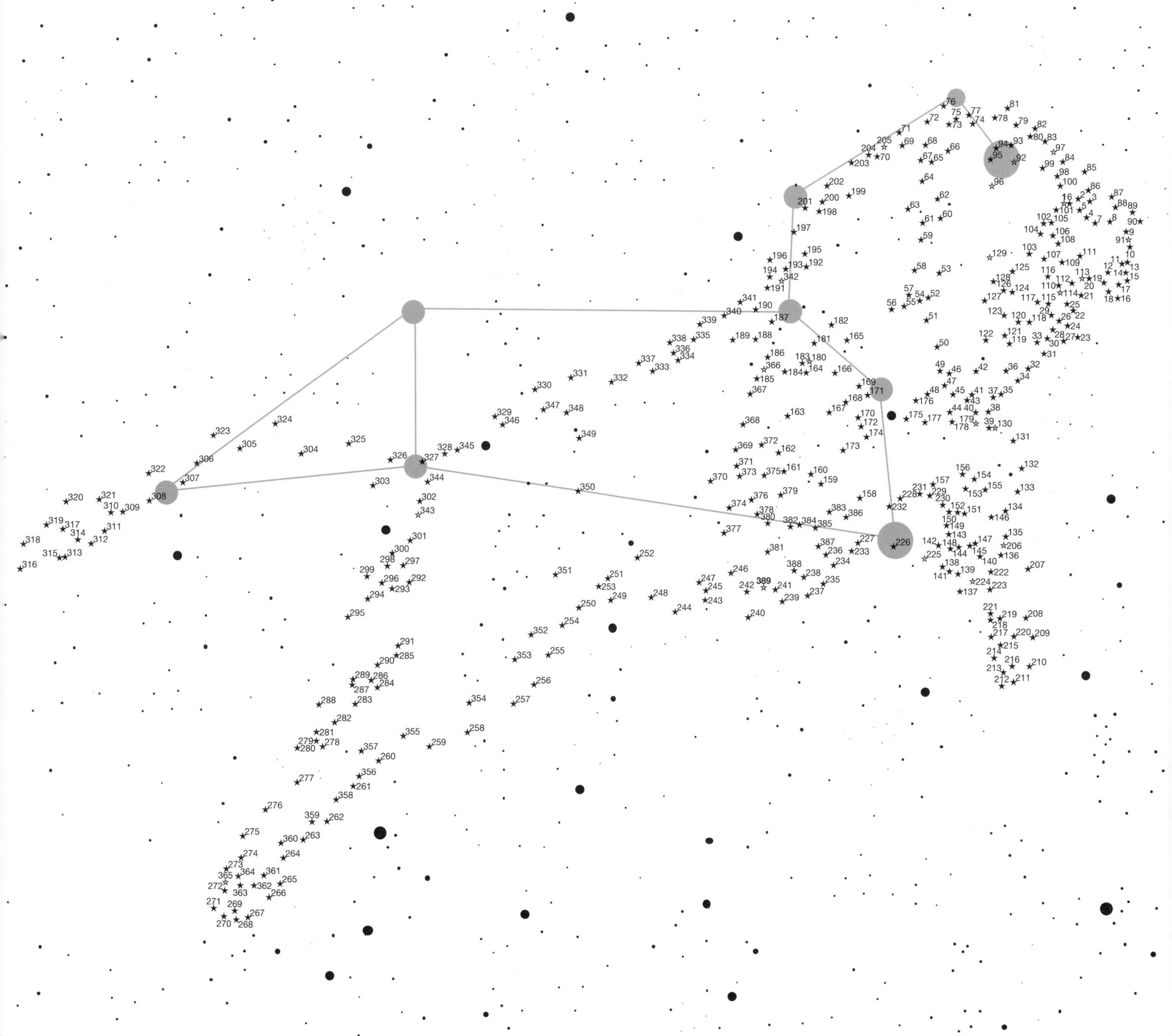

VIRGO

Virgo is the largest of the zodiacal constellations and the second largest in the sky (after Hydra). Identified with goddesses of fertility and justice, Virgo is represented as a young maiden carrying an ear of wheat. She is located next to Libra, 'The Weighing Scales'.

VIRGO AT A GLANCE

What does its name mean?
'The Virgin' in Latin

Which is the brightest star?
Spica (Alpha Virginis)

Where does this constellation lie?
In the Northern and Southern Hemispheres

To which constellation family does it belong?
The zodiac

* IN MYTHOLOGY

In Greek mythology, Virgo represents both justice and harvest. One story tells of a maiden associated with the spring, Persephone, kidnapped by the god of the underworld, Hades. Persephone's mother, Demeter, goddess of the harvest, let the world turn cold and barren in her despair. When Zeus agreed to rescue Persephone, he insisted that she must eat nothing in the underworld. However, tricked by Hades, Persephone sucked on a pomegranate seed. As punishment, the maiden had to return to the underworld for a few months every year, which is when winter returns to the Earth.

* IN THE ZODIAC

Dates: 23rd August – 22nd September

Characteristics: caring and hard-working

Zodiac symbol: ♍

PORRIMA (GAMMA VIRGINIS) is a binary star that is named after a Roman goddess.

STAR FACT

The Virgo Cluster is a collection of over 1,300 galaxies about 54 million light years away from our Solar System. Amazingly, the brightest galaxies can be viewed through a pair of binoculars.

SPICA (ALPHA VIRGINIS) is the brightest star in Virgo. Latin for 'ear of wheat', Spica marks the wheat held in the maiden's hand.

LIBRA

Libra represents a set of scales – the Romans viewed Libra as the scales of justice, held aloft by neighbouring Virgo. The Ancient Greeks saw Libra as the 'claws' of Scorpius, which also lies next to Libra.

LIBRA AT A GLANCE

What does its name mean?
'The Weighing Scales' in Latin

Which is the brightest star?
Zubeneschamali (Beta Librae)

Where does this constellation lie?
It is visible in the Southern Hemisphere during summer and in the Northern Hemisphere in winter

To which constellation family does it belong?
The zodiac

* IN MYTHOLOGY

Myth tells of Dike, the Greek goddess of justice, who lived during the Golden Age of mankind, a time of peace and good health, fertile crops and eternal youth. However, humans became greedy. They began warring with each other and lost their respect for the gods. Enraged, Dike left Earth and flew into the sky, becoming the constellation Virgo, from where she looks down scornfully on mankind, with her balance scales, as Libra, close by.

* IN THE ZODIAC

Dates: 23rd September – 22nd October

Characteristics: kind, gentle and fair

Zodiac symbol: ♎

ZUBENELGENUBI (ALPHA LIBRAE) is actually a double star†. Its Arabic name means 'southern claw'.

ZUBENESCHAMALI (BETA LIBRAE) comes from Arabic words for 'northern claw' – the claw of Scorpius – and is Libra's brightest star.

BRACHIUM (SIGMA LIBRAE) represents one of the weighing pans of Libra's scales. Its traditional name means 'arm' in Latin.

460 150
461 151 459 149
490 462 148 119
489 492 491 118 117 120
488 493 464 463 147 146 121
476 477 152 458 133 134 116
486 487 465 475 478 153 457 132 135 145 122
494 474 472 471 139 138 136 115 123
485 505 466 144 104 124
473 470 479 553 131 140 137
432 431 429 504 495 467 105 143 103
428 506 484 114 125 181 180 179 178 177
436 434 433 424 425 430 427 502 468 469 141 107
435 426 142 130 182 183 184 185 176 175 174 173
437 507 501 496 102 113 108 101 191 192 172
440 439 438 423 419 420 510 509 508 483 503 497 112 106 126 190 189 186 171 170 169
442 511 421 422 448 449 500 545 554 552 312 109 188 187 167
441 443 418 447 450 499 498 480 456 154 129 111 110 161 193 162 163 168 166
444 445 446 512 482 455 313 155 127 160 164 165
417 481 544 311 128 100
454 156
451 542 543 159
513 314 315 194
546 555 551 310
452 453 157 158
99
416
514
98
415
56 528 57 529 530
373 570 374 571 547 556 550 309 55 58 531
372 572
195
375 97
414 45 44
517 515 371 573 54 59 532
362 361 198 199 46
518 363 376 196 93 61
519 516 360 200 43 527 96 92 60
378 574 197 47 94 534 62
370 364 410 413 409 377 201 53 42 526 91 535 533
359 379
520 577 90
548 297 549 296 308
407 408 411 576 89 6 7 95
406 63
412 578 575 298 557 303 525 536
579 380 304 5 537
369 365 358 305 295 41 3 8
321 580 299 48 52 2 20
317 318 320 336 322 405 306 307 302 202 88 4
337 300 292 524 27 26
368 357 319 283 284 301 291 293 40 1
404 344 343 316 51 87 25 64
402 538 403 342 290 9
367 398 366 356 539 349 348 345 338 381 285 523 85 86 522 32 31 28
397 399 401 323 294 50 81 49 39 82 84
540 282 289 80 24
335 33 30
400 350 347 341 203 65
83 10
382 286 521 12
355 541 324 288 38 21
339 334 22 19
326 281 287 13 66
396 79
34 11 23
351 333 325 340 327 383 204 29
18
354 346 332 37 14 67
35
280 205
395 17 36
328 384 352 78 77
394 353 331
15
329 279 76 68
393
16
385 73 69
330 74
75
391 390 386
392
206 70
278 72
389 387 207
277 71
388
276 208
275
209
562
558
569 561
559
560
274 210
563
568
273 564
567 211
566 565
272
214 213 265 212
271 233
215
270 264
216 269
266 263 234 232
256 217 248 231
262 268 239 230
219 218 257 235 252
220 247 261 240 229
249 251 255
246 258 236
238
253 267 260
221 245 250 254 237 241 228
242 259
244 243
227
222
223 226
224 225

SCORPIUS

With its long, graceful shape, Scorpius is a spectacular constellation. It represents the scorpion sent to kill Orion in Greek mythology. Its brightest star, Antares, is located at the scorpion's 'heart' and the curve of stars at the end clearly mark its stinging 'tail'.

* IN MYTHOLOGY

In one version of the Greek myths, a scorpion was sent by Gaia, the Earth goddess, to kill Orion, who was boasting about his hunting skills. Another tale tells of the god Apollo, who, angry at Orion for claiming to be a better hunter than Apollo's brother, Artemis, sent a scorpion to kill him. Zeus, king of the gods, put Orion and the scorpion to rest in the heavens, but made sure they were placed at opposite ends of the sky. To this day, these constellations are visible at different times of the year.

* IN THE ZODIAC

Dates: 23rd October – 22nd November

Characteristics: brave, passionate and fiercely independent

Zodiac symbol: ♏

SCORPIUS AT A GLANCE

What does its name mean?
'The Scorpion' in Latin

Which is the brightest star?
Antares

Where does this constellation lie?
In the Southern Hemisphere

To which constellation family does it belong?
The zodiac

LESATH (UPSILON SCORPII) forms part of the scorpion's tail. The tail passes through the glowing band of stars that is known as the Milky Way† – the galaxy that our Solar System is part of.

SHAULA (LAMBDA SCORPII) is located at the scorpion's tail and named after the Arabic word for 'raised tail'.

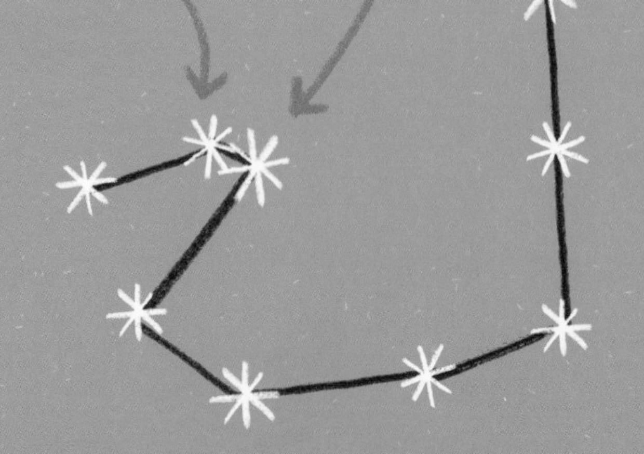

ANTARES is a supergiant star that is 10,000 times brighter than our Sun. Its name means 'rival to Mars', because of its distinctive orange-red colour.

STAR FACT

Not all cultures have viewed Scorpius as a scorpion. On the island of Hawaii, the stars are seen as the ancient chief Maui's 'fishhook'; in Chinese mythology, the constellation forms part of a group of stars called the Azure Dragon.

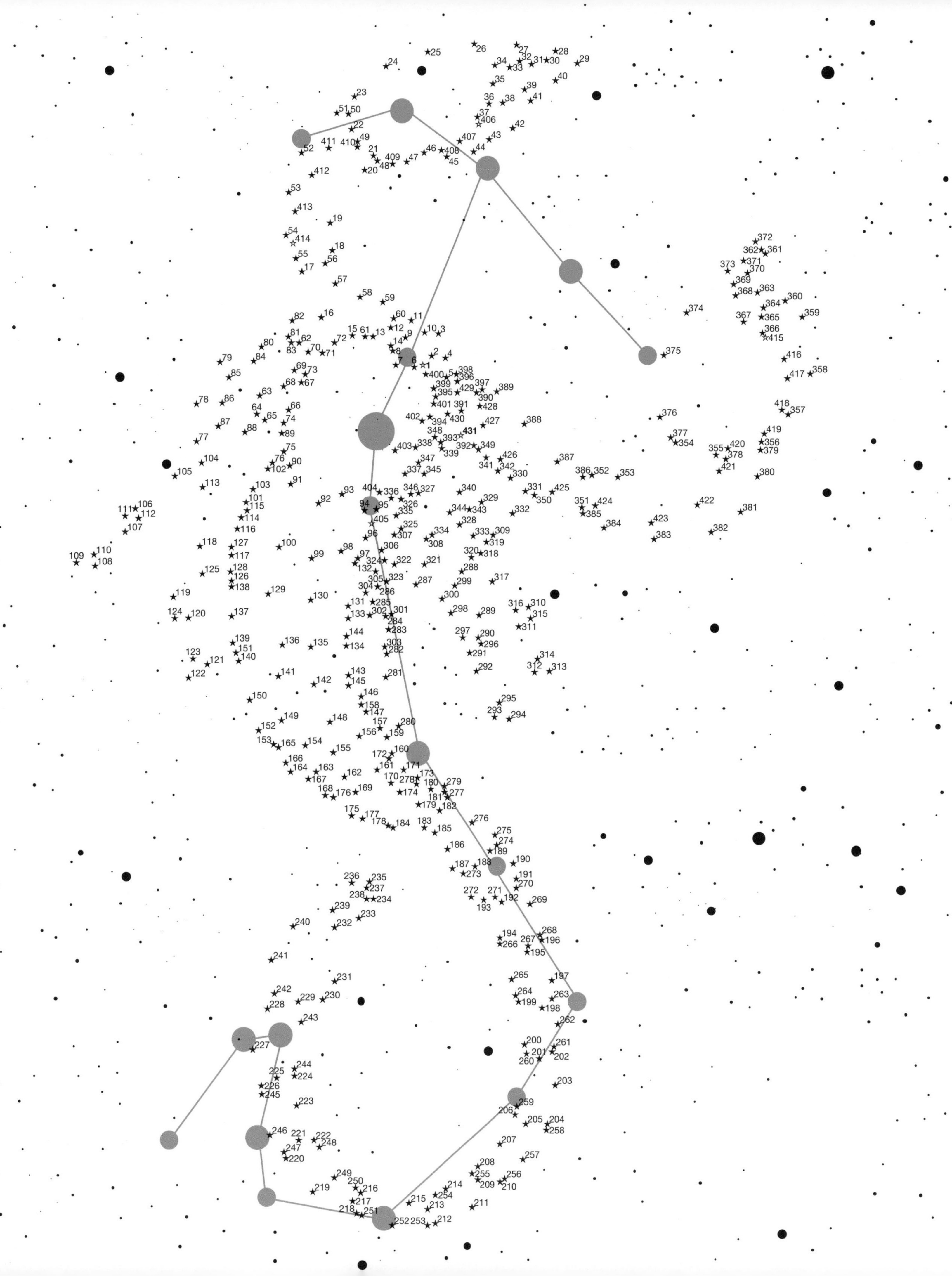

SAGITTARIUS

Sagittarius lies in the Southern Celestial Hemisphere†. It depicts a centaur – a man with the body and legs of a horse – drawing back his bow. The constellation is easy to identify because its brightest stars form an asterism known as 'the Teapot'.

SAGITTARIUS AT A GLANCE

What does its name mean?
'The Archer' in Latin

Which is the brightest star?
Kaus Australis

Where does this constellation lie?
In the Southern Hemisphere

To which constellation family does it belong?
The zodiac

* IN MYTHOLOGY

Centaurs originate in Babylonian mythology. Some Ancient Greek myths associate Sagittarius with Crotus the 'satyr' – a skilled huntsman who was part man, part goat, and the inventor of archery.

Another Greek myth links Sagittarius with the story of Orion and a scorpion. When the scorpion was sent to kill Orion, the archer was ordered to shoot the poisonous creature with his arrow. The archer is seen as aiming his bow towards the heart – the brightest star, Antares – of the neighbouring Scorpius constellation.

* IN THE ZODIAC

Dates: 22nd November – 21st December

Characteristics: enthusiastic, good sense of humour, loves travel

Zodiac symbol: ♐

NUNKI (SIGMA SAGITTARII)
is the second brightest star and forms part of the Teapot asterism.

THE TEAPOT
is an easily recognizable

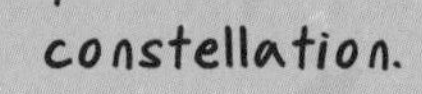

group of stars in this constellation.

KAUS AUSTRALIS (EPSILON SAGITTARII)

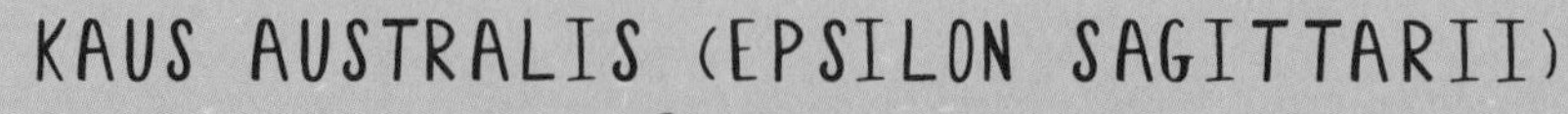

is the brightest star in Sagittarius and marks the base of the archer's bow. The Arabic word 'kaus' means 'bow'.

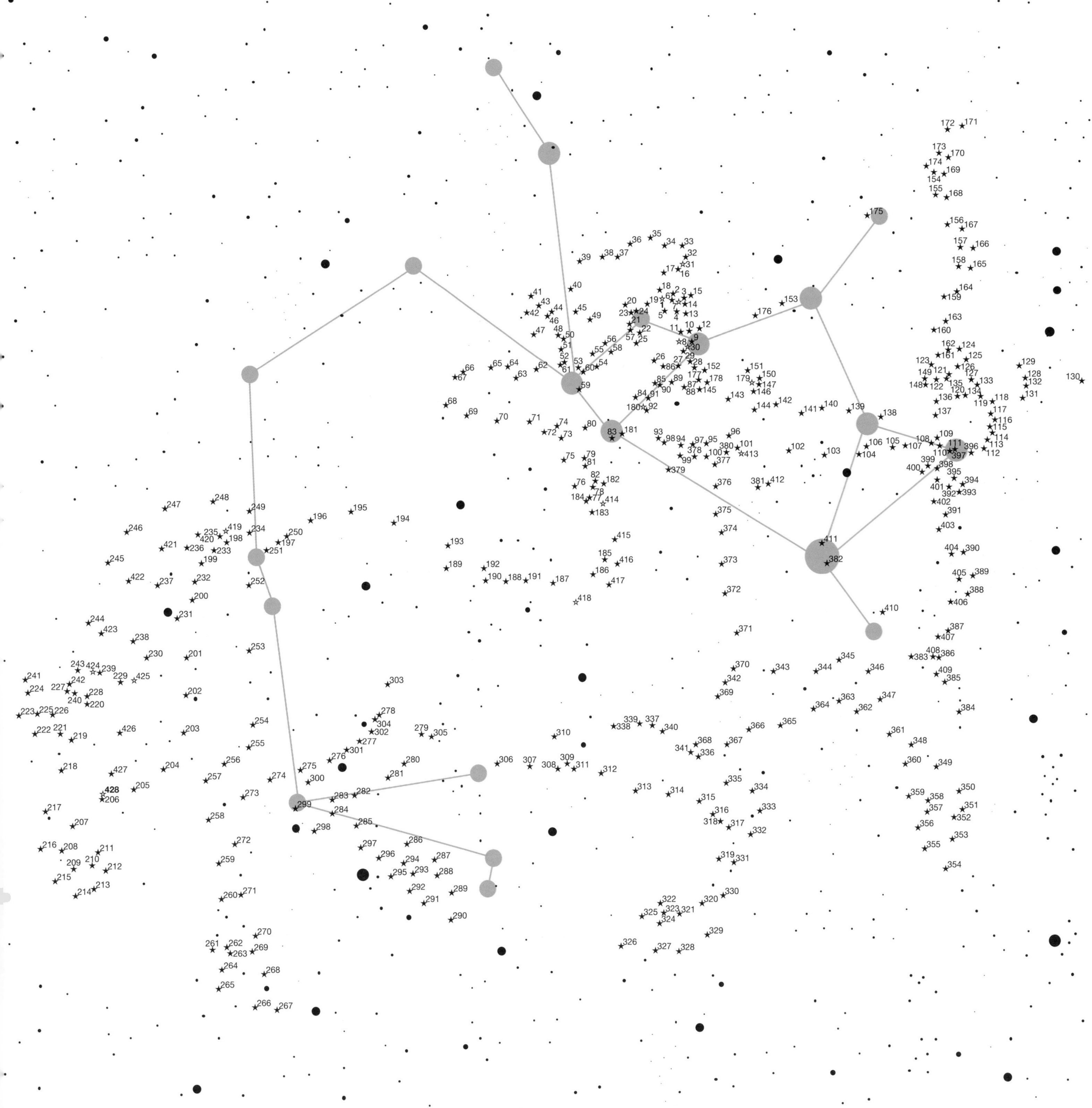

CYGNUS

Cygnus, 'The Swan', is one of the Northern Hemisphere's brightest constellations. With its long neck and outspread wings, this star pattern is unmistakable. Cygnus also contains The Northern Cross, a well-known asterism.

CYGNUS AT A GLANCE

What does its name mean?
'The Swan' in Latin

Which is the brightest star?
Deneb (Alpha Cygni)

Where does this constellation lie?
In the Northern Hemisphere

To which constellation family does it belong?
Hercules

* IN MYTHOLOGY

Cygnus is often associated with the story of Zeus, king of the gods, and Queen Leda of Sparta. Zeus was in love with the beautiful Leda. One day, she was attacked by an eagle. To save her, Zeus disguised himself as a swan and protected her under his wings. The couple fell in love and had twins and Zeus placed a swan in the sky to celebrate the birth of their children.

* AROUND THE WORLD

Other cultures also recognized Cygnus as a bird-like creature:

- Tonga, Polynesia: 'Tula-luupe', meaning 'pigeon perch'
- China: 'Que Qiao', meaning 'magpie bridge'

ALBIREO (BETA CYGNI)

Through a telescope Albireo is a beautiful gold and blue double star. It marks the head of the swan and is sometimes known as the 'beak star'.

DENEB (ALPHA CYGNI)

is the 19th brightest star in the sky and is around 200 times larger than our Sun.

STAR FACT

Part of our galaxy, the Milky Way, can be seen as a band of light across the night sky. The brightest region of the Milky Way in the Northern Hemisphere runs right through Cygnus.

SADR (GAMMA CYGNI)

is located at the intersection of the Northern Cross. Its name means 'the chest' in Arabic.

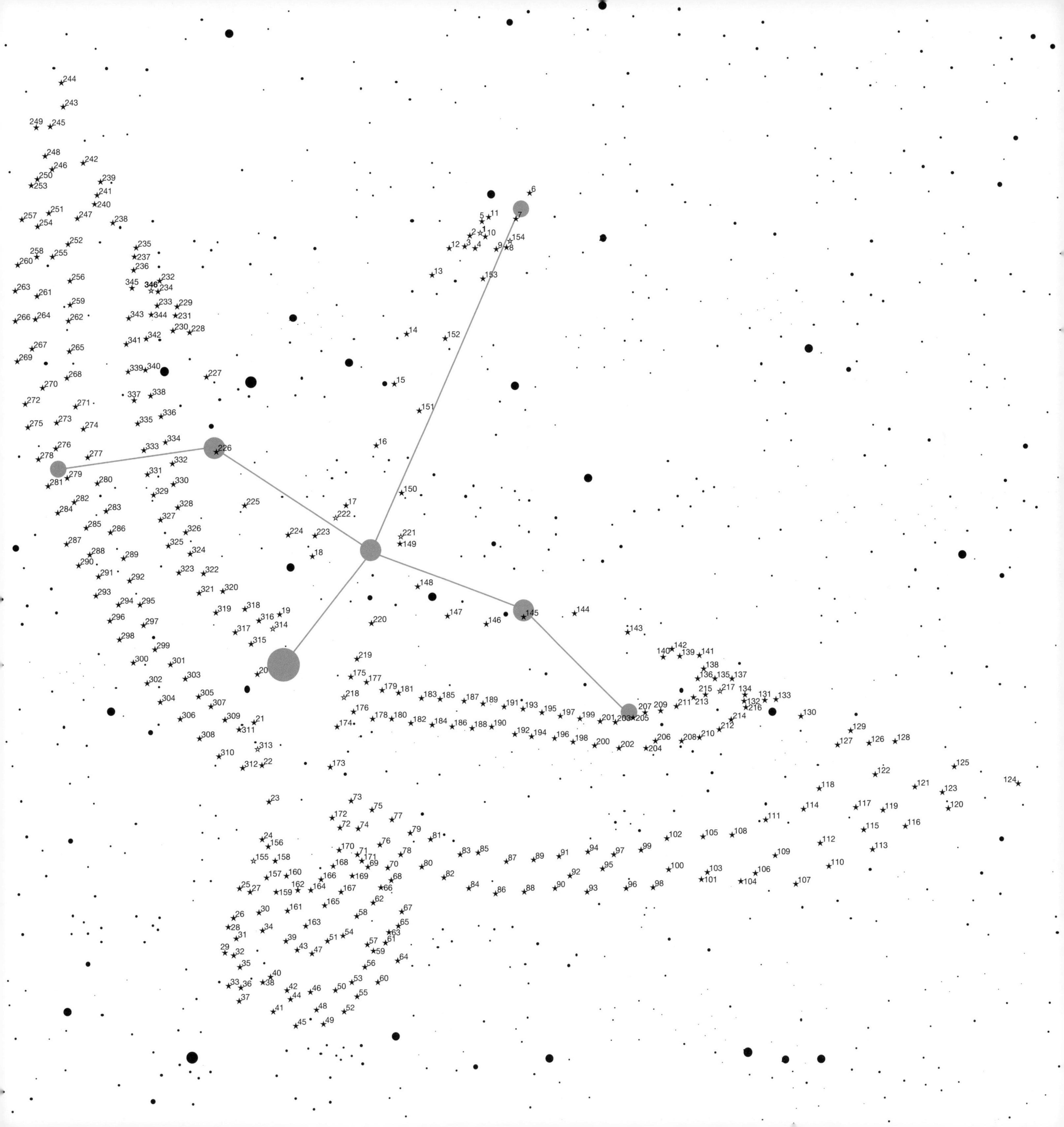

244
243
249 245
248 242
246
250 239
253
241
240 5 11
257 251 247 238 7 6
254
2 1 10 154
252 235 12 3 4 9 8
258 255 237
260
236
256 13 153
263 345 346 232
261 234
259 233 229
266 264 262 343 344 231
230 228 14 152
267 341 342
269 265
268 339 340 227
270 15
272 337 338
271 151
275 273 274 335 336
276 334 16
278 277 333 226
279
281 280 331 332
330 150
329
284 282 283 328 17
225
327 222
285 286 326 221
287 325 224 223 149
288 289 324 18
290
291 323 322
292
293 321 320 148
294 295
319 318 19 147
296 297 316 314 145 144
317 146
298 220 143
315
142
299 140 139 141
300 301 219 138
20
302 303 175 177 136 135 137
179 181 215 217 134
304 305 218 183 185 187 189 191 193 131 133
307 195 197 199 207 209 211 213 132
176 216
306 309 21 178 180 182 184 186 188 190 201 203 205 214 130
174 212 129
311 192 194 196 198 206 208 210
308 313 200 202 127 126 128
204
310
312 22 173
125
122
118 121 123 124
23 73
75 114 117 119 120
172 77
72 74 111
116
79 115
24 81 102 105 108
156 76 112
170 78 83 85 113
155 158 71 171 97 99 109
69 70 87 89 91 94
157 160 80 100 103 106 110
168 169 95
162 166 68 82 92 101 104 107
25 27 164 66 84 96 98
159 167 86 88 90 93
62
165
161 67
26 30 58
163 65
28 34 63
31 39 61
51 54 57
29 32 43 47 59
64
35 56
40
33 36 38 42 53 60
50
46 55
44
37
48 52
41
49
45

ORION

Orion is a magnificent constellation, renowned throughout the world. It's easy to make out the shape of this famous figure from Greek mythology in the sky – Orion's raised club and shield and the line of three stars known as 'Orion's Belt'.

ORION AT A GLANCE

What does its name mean?
Orion is the name of a famous hunter from Greek mythology

Which is the brightest star?
Rigel

Where does this constellation lie?
This constellation can be seen in the Northern Hemisphere from late autumn to early spring and in the Southern Hemisphere during summer

To which constellation family does it belong?
Orion

* IN MYTHOLOGY

The story of Orion has many different versions. In one tale, the hunter Orion was the most handsome of men, but also the most arrogant. He boasted that he could kill any creature on Earth. On hearing him, the Earth goddess, Gaia, sent a giant scorpion to kill him as punishment for his arrogance.

* AROUND THE WORLD

Cultures around the world also viewed Orion as a powerful, male figure:

- Ancient Egypt: Osiris, the god of the afterlife
- Babylonia: 'the Heavenly Shepherd'
- Hungary: Nimrod, a famous hunter
- China: Shen, a great warrior

STAR FACT

An image of (what is believed to be) the Orion constellation from around 32,000 years ago was found engraved on an ivory tablet in Germany.

BETELGEUSE (ALPHA ORIONIS)

Famous for its vivid orange colour, this star lies on the hunter's right shoulder. It is a supergiant star destined to blow itself up in a supernova† one day.

ORION'S BELT

is a well-known and easily recognizable asterism.

ORION NEBULA†

lies on the lower half of Orion and is one of the brightest nebulae in the sky.

RIGEL (BETA ORIONIS)

is the constellation's brightest star at around 40,000 times brighter than our Sun and is a vivid blue-white colour.

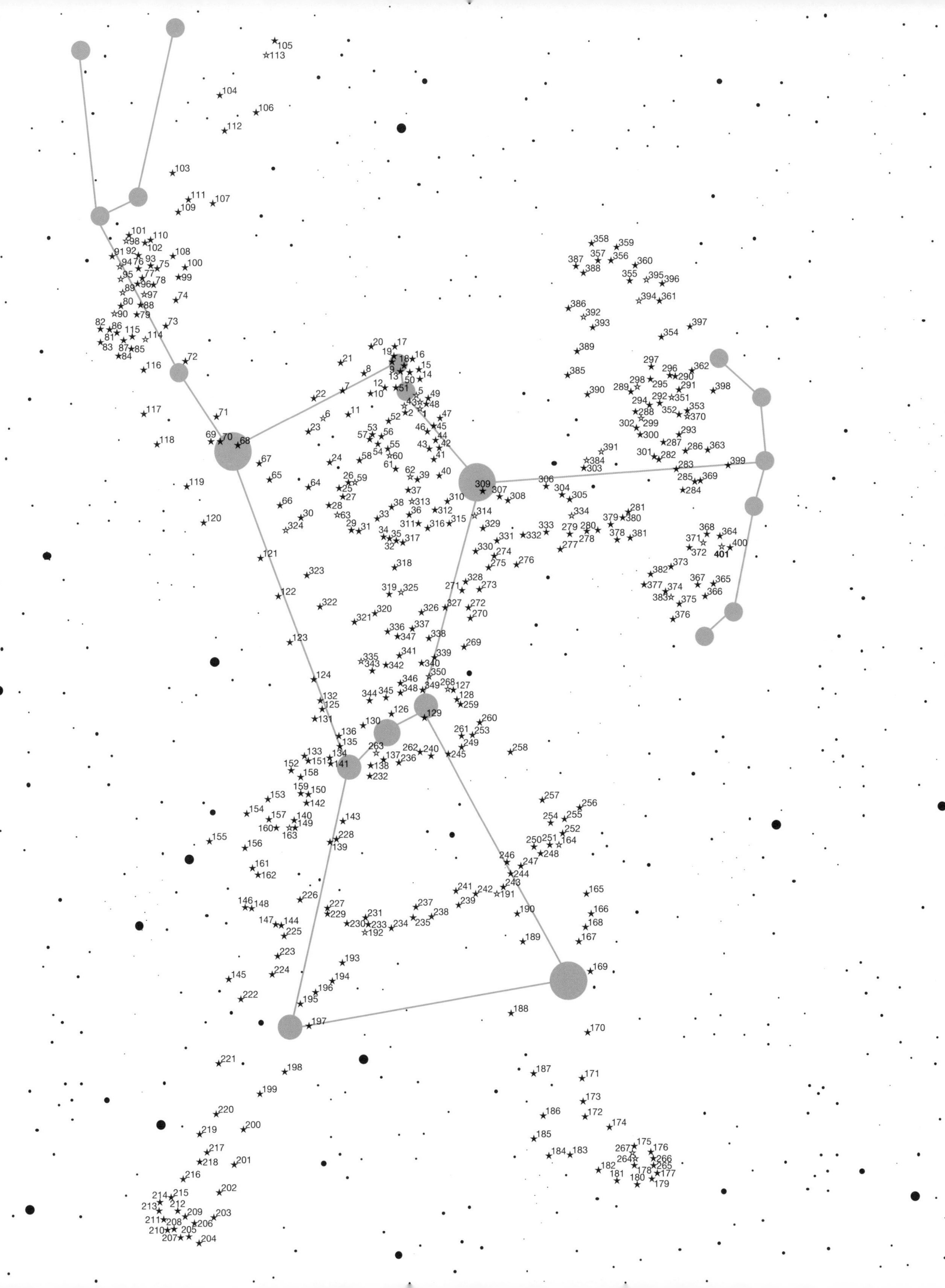

URSA MAJOR

Ursa Major, one of the largest constellations in the northern sky, means 'The Great Bear'. It has been the subject of many myths and legends dating back to ancient times. The asterism known as 'The Plough' or 'The Big Dipper' makes up part of Ursa Major.

URSA MAJOR AT A GLANCE

What does its name mean?
'The Great Bear' in Latin

Which is the brightest star?
Alioth

Where does this constellation lie?
In the Northern Hemisphere

To which constellation family does it belong?
Ursa Major

* IN MYTHOLOGY

According to the ancient Greeks, Callisto was a beautiful maiden. When Zeus, king of the gods, saw her, he fell instantly in love. The couple had a son, named Arcas, but Hera, Zeus' wife, was enraged by her husband's betrayal. In revenge, she turned Callisto into a bear. For years, Callisto roamed the forest until one day, she came face to face with her long-lost son. Arcas was about to kill the bear, but Zeus stepped in to stop him. The god sent both Callisto and Arcas into the sky as the Ursa Major and nearby Ursa Minor constellations.

* AROUND THE WORLD

Cultures around the world associated Ursa Major and The Plough with different forms:

- Romans: 'Septentrio' – oxen and plough
- Hindus: 'Sapta Rishi' – the Seven Sages (wise beings)
- Dutch: 'Steelpannetje' – the saucepan

DUBHE (ALPHA URSAE MAJORIS)
is the second brightest star in Ursa Major, and means 'bear' in Arabic.

PINWHEEL GALAXY

ALIOTH (EPSILON URSAE MAJORIS)
is Ursa Major's brightest star, around 80 light years from our Sun.

STAR FACT

Ursa Major contains one of the best-known spiral galaxies in the night sky, the Pinwheel Galaxy. With its distinctive spiral arms and bright central region, it is home to many billions of stars.

THE PLOUGH (OR THE BIG DIPPER)
is the most visible part of the Ursa Major constellation, made up of its seven brightest stars.

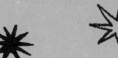

PEGASUS

Pegasus, one of the largest constellations, represents a winged horse in Greek mythology. It is known for 'The Great Square of Pegasus', an asterism formed by its three brightest stars. The Great Square's fourth star, Alpheratz, is part of a nearby constellation, Andromeda.

PEGASUS AT A GLANCE

What does its name mean?
Name of a flying horse in Greek mythology

Which is the brightest star?
Enif (Epsilon Pegasi)

Where does this constellation lie?
In the Northern Hemisphere

To which constellation family does it belong?
Perseus

* IN MYTHOLOGY

Pegasus was a handsome winged horse that was captured and tamed by the hero Bellerophon. Pegasus helped Bellerophon in many of his heroic deeds, including killing the fire-breathing monster, Chimera. Feeling full of himself, Bellerophon flew up to Mount Olympus, hoping to join the gods. But he fell off Pegasus on the way, and landed back on Earth. Pegasus continued the journey and reached Olympus, where the god Zeus placed him among the stars.

* AROUND THE WORLD

The Square of Pegasus has also been known as:

- builder's stars (China)
- a bedstead (India)
- a cooking grill (Guyana, South America)

ENIF (EPSILON PEGASI) is the brightest star in the Pegasus constellation. Arabic for 'nose', it marks the horse's muzzle.

MARKAB (ALPHA PEGASI) is the brightest star in the Great Square of Pegasus. Its Arabic name means 'saddle of the horse'.

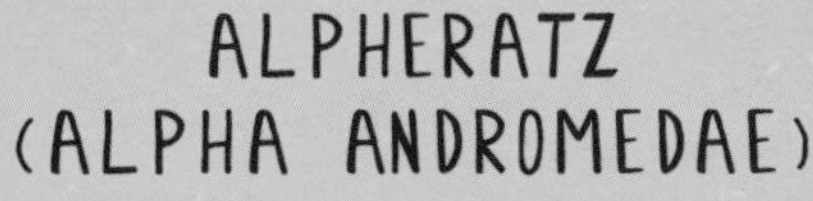

ALPHERATZ (ALPHA ANDROMEDAE) belongs to the Andromeda constellation, and marks the fourth star in the Square of Pegasus.

THE GREAT SQUARE OF PEGASUS is one of the most recognisable asterisms in the night sky.

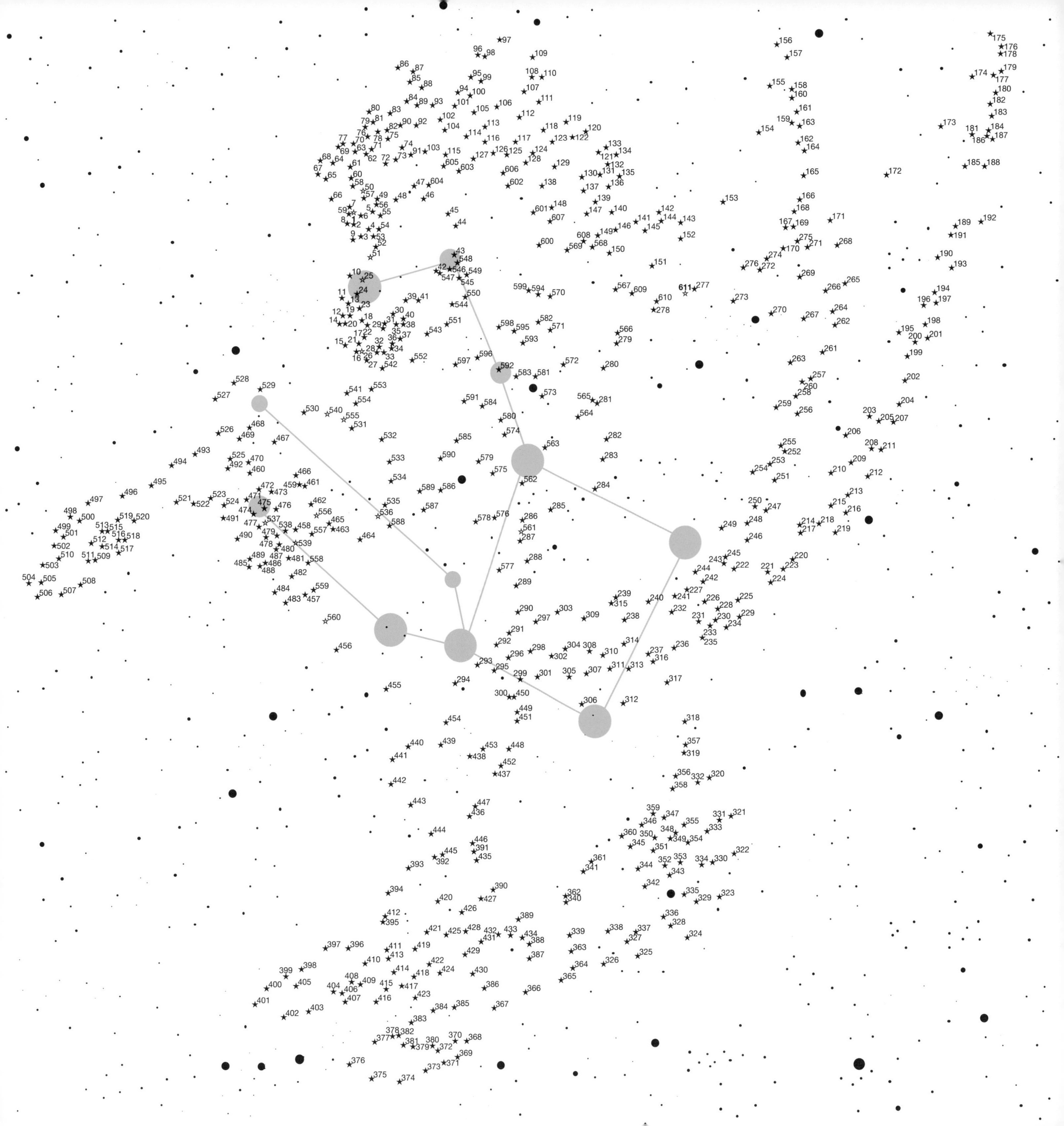

CASSIOPEIA

The Cassiopeia constellation is named after a vain and boastful queen from Greek mythology. Cassiopeia is depicted as sitting on a throne combing her hair, though this shape is hard to see. More noticeable is a 'W' shape, made up of several bright stars.

CASSIOPEIA AT A GLANCE

What does its name mean?
Name of the queen of Ethiopia from Greek mythology

Which is the brightest star?
Schedar (Alpha Cassiopeiae)

Where does this constellation lie?
In the Northern Hemisphere

To which constellation family does it belong?
Perseus

* IN MYTHOLOGY

Cassiopeia, wife of King Cepheus and mother to Princess Andromeda, boasted to the sea nymphs that she was more beautiful than them. Outraged, the nymphs convinced the sea god Poseidon to punish Cassiopeia by sending a sea monster to destroy her kingdom. To stop the sea monster, Cepheus offered his daughter as a sacrifice. He chained Andromeda to a rock. She was rescued by the hero Perseus. It is said that as further punishment for Cassiopeia's vanity, Poseidon placed her in the sky, spinning around for eternity.

* AROUND THE WORLD

Other cultures viewed Cassiopeia as an animal, rather than a human figure, such as:

- spider (Native American region of Southwest USA)
- moose (Scandinavia)
- whale's tail (Marshall Islands, in the central Pacific Ocean)

SEGIN (EPSILON CASSIOPEIAE) is more than 2,500 times brighter than our Sun.

CIH (GAMMA CASSIOPEIAE) is the central star in Cassiopeia's 'W' shape. The star spins very rapidly and varies in brightness.

RUCHBAH (DELTA CASSIOPEIAE) is a binary star. The name comes from the Arabic word for 'knee'.

SCHEDAR (ALPHA CASSIOPEIAE) is an orange giant star and is the brightest star in the constellation.

STAR FACT

The Pacman Nebula, named after a video game character, is a large gas cloud that lies in the Cassiopeia constellation. The dark areas of the nebula are thought to look like Pacman's open mouth.

CRUX

The Crux constellation contains 'The Southern Cross', the most familiar star pattern in the Southern Hemisphere. Its four bright stars have been recognized by many cultures for thousands of years. Crux is the smallest of the 88 modern constellations.

CRUX AT A GLANCE

What does its name mean?
'The Cross' in Latin

Which is the brightest star?
Acrux (Alpha Crucis)

Where does this constellation lie?
In the Southern Hemisphere

To which constellation family does it belong?
Hercules

* IN MYTHOLOGY

Crux was mostly unknown to the Greeks and Romans. From around 400 CE†, the constellation was no longer visible in the Northern Hemisphere. However, since prehistoric times, it has featured in Australian Aboriginal storytelling. Some Aboriginal people tell of the Emu in the Sky, a great bird with the Southern Cross at its head. The Emu looks different at different times of year: when it looks like it is running across the sky, emu eggs are ready to collect. When the Emu's head is low on the horizon, it is seated in a waterhole, meaning the waterholes are full of water.

* AROUND THE WORLD

Other interpretations of The Southern Cross:

- stair (Peru, by the Inca people of the 1300s–1500s)
- anchor (Maoris of New Zealand)
- duck (Tonga, Polynesia)
- triggerfish (Samoa, Polynesia)

GACRUX (GAMMA CRUCIS) is often used in navigation, as tracing a line from Gacrux to Acrux (below) leads to a point close to the Southern Celestial Pole.

ACRUX (ALPHA CRUCIS) is the brightest star in the constellation and the 13th brightest star in the night sky.

MIMOSA (BETA CRUCIS) Its name might refer to the star's blue-white colour, similar to some mimosa flowers.

STAR FACT

The Southern Cross features on the flags of several countries in the Southern Hemisphere, including Australia, New Zealand, Brazil and Papua New Guinea.

1 2 3 4 5 6 7 8 9 10 11 12 13 14 15 16 17 18 19 20 21 22 23 24 25 26 27 28 29 30 31 32 33 34 35 36 37 38 39 40 41 42 43 44 45 46 47 48 49 50 51 52 53 54 55 56 57 58 59 60 61 62 63 64 65 66 67 68 69 70 71 72 73 74 75 76 77 78 79 80 81 82 83 84 85 86 87 88 89 90 91 92 93 94 95 96 97 98 99 100 101 102 103 104 105 106 107 108 109 110 111 112 113 114 115 116 117 118 119 120 121 122 123 124 125 126 127 128 129 130 131 132 133 134 135 136 137 138 139 140 141 142 143 144 145 146 147 148 149 150 151 152 153 154 155 156 157 158 159 160 161 162 163 164 165 166 167 168 169 170 171 172 173 174 175 176 177 178 179 180 181 182 183 184 185 186 187 188 189 190 191 192 193 194 195 196 197 198 199 200 201 202 203 204 205 206 207 208 209 210 211 212 213 214 215 216 217 218 219 220 221 222 223 224 225 226 227 228 229 230 231 232 233 234 235 236 237 238 239 240 241 242 243 244 245 246 247 248 249 250 251 252 253 254 255 256 257 258 259 260 261 262 263 264 265 266 267 268 269 270 271 272 273 274 275 276 277 278 279 280 281 282 283 284 285 286 287 288 289 290 291 292 293 294 295 296 297 298 299 300

HERCULES

Hercules might be one of the largest constellations, but it is not one of the brightest and can be tricky to spot in the night sky. It is identified with the mighty Roman hero Hercules, or Heracles to the Greeks, who is seen as standing over a slain dragon, holding a club.

HERCULES AT A GLANCE

What does its name mean?
Hercules is the Roman name for Heracles, the famous strong man from Greek mythology

Which is the brightest star?
Kornephoros (Beta Herculis)

Where does this constellation lie?
In the Northern Hemisphere

To which constellation family does it belong?
Hercules

* IN MYTHOLOGY

In the Greek myth, Heracles, a warrior of great strength, was given 12 Labours, or tasks, to complete as punishment for killing his family while under an evil spell. In the Eleventh Labour, Heracles had to take the Golden Apples from the Garden of Hesperides, which was guarded by the multi-headed dragon, Ladon. Armed with his club, Heracles defeated the dragon and stole off with the Golden Apples. The dragon was then placed in the sky as the nearby constellation Draco.

* AROUND THE WORLD

Other heroic figures from ancient civilizations that are sometimes associated with Hercules:

- Gilgamesh, a demigod of great strength (Sumer, an ancient civilization from around 4000 BCE)
- Heryshaf, the ram-god (ancient Egypt)
- Melqart, a Phoenician god (Phoenicia, an eastern Mediterranean civilization from around 1000 BCE)

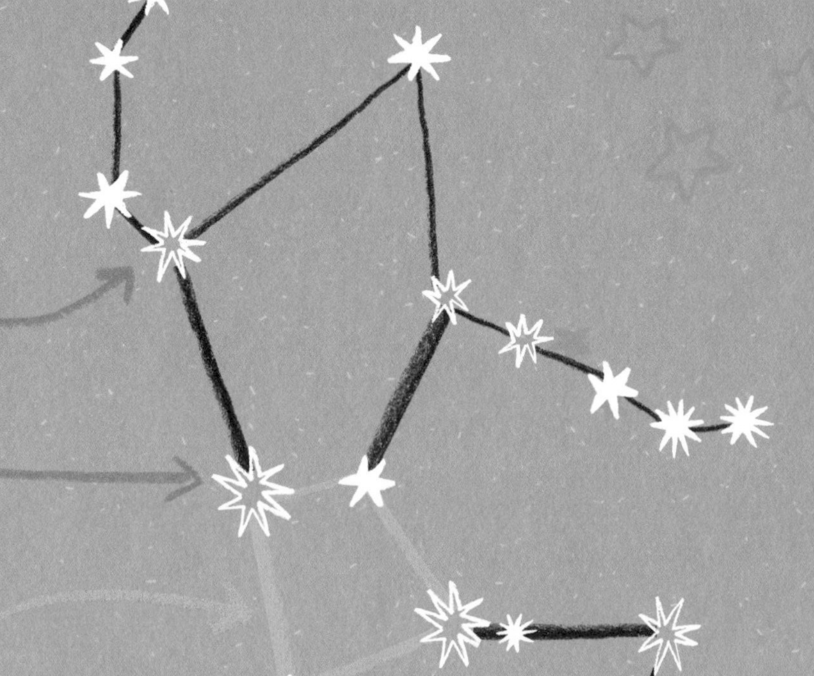

KORNEPHOROS (BETA HERCULIS)

is the brightest star in the Hercules constellation. Its name comes from the Greek for 'club bearer' and marks Hercules' armpit.

ZETA HERCULIS

is the brightest star in the Keystone asterism.

THE KEYSTONE

is a square-shaped asterism that represents Hercules' torso.

STAR FACT

The Great Globular Cluster in Hercules, located on the side of the 'Keystone', is one of the brightest globular star clusters† in the northern sky, containing around 300,000 stars. Even without binoculars, the Cluster can be seen as a small, fuzzy spot in the sky.

LEPUS

Lepus, 'The Hare', can be seen leaping at the feet of Orion in the Southern Hemisphere. Lepus is often depicted as dashing across the sky to escape Orion's fast-footed hunting dogs, the nearby constellations of Canis Major and Canis Minor.

IN MYTHOLOGY

According to one Greek story, a man brought a pregnant hare to the island of Leros to keep as a pet. The hare had her babies, and soon, everyone was breeding hares. But the animals began to overrun the island. They ate all the crops, and the islanders almost starved. The people got together and managed to rid the island of the pesky creatures. After that, the gods put an image of a hare in the sky to remind the people that too much of a good thing doesn't always lead to happiness.

AROUND THE WORLD

Lepus has been depicted as:

- camels drinking water out of the Milky Way 'river' (Arab lands)
- a shed (China)
- the boat of Osiris, an Egyptian god (ancient Egypt)

LEPUS AT A GLANCE

What does its name mean?
'The Hare' in Latin

Which is the brightest star?
Arneb (Alpha Leporis)

Where does this constellation lie?
In the Southern Hemisphere

To which constellation family does it belong?
Orion

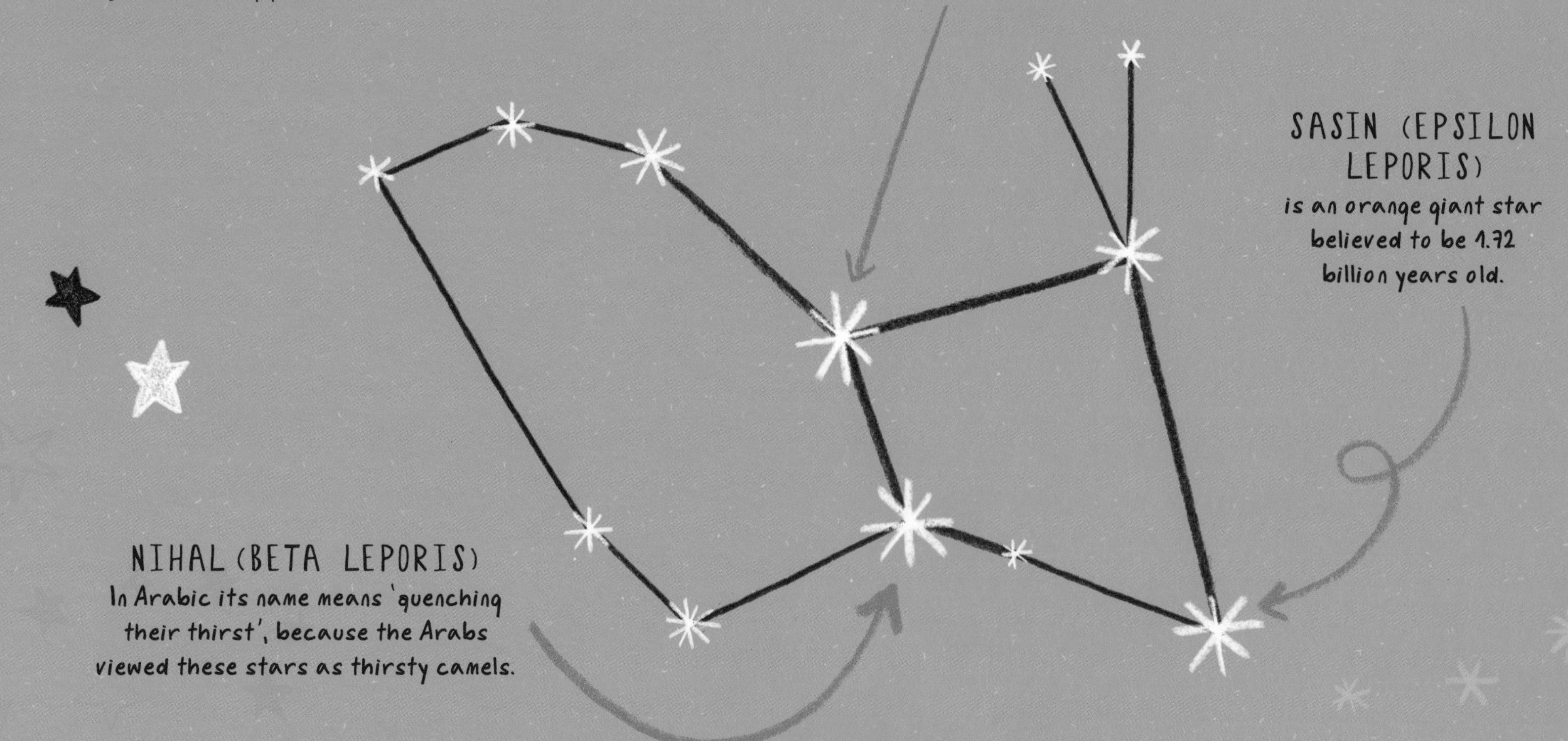

ARNEB (ALPHA LEPORIS)
comes from an Arabic word for 'hare'. It is the brightest star in Lepus.
SASIN (EPSILON LEPORIS)
is an orange giant star believed to be 1.72 billion years old.
NIHAL (BETA LEPORIS)
In Arabic its name means 'quenching their thirst', because the Arabs viewed these stars as thirsty camels.

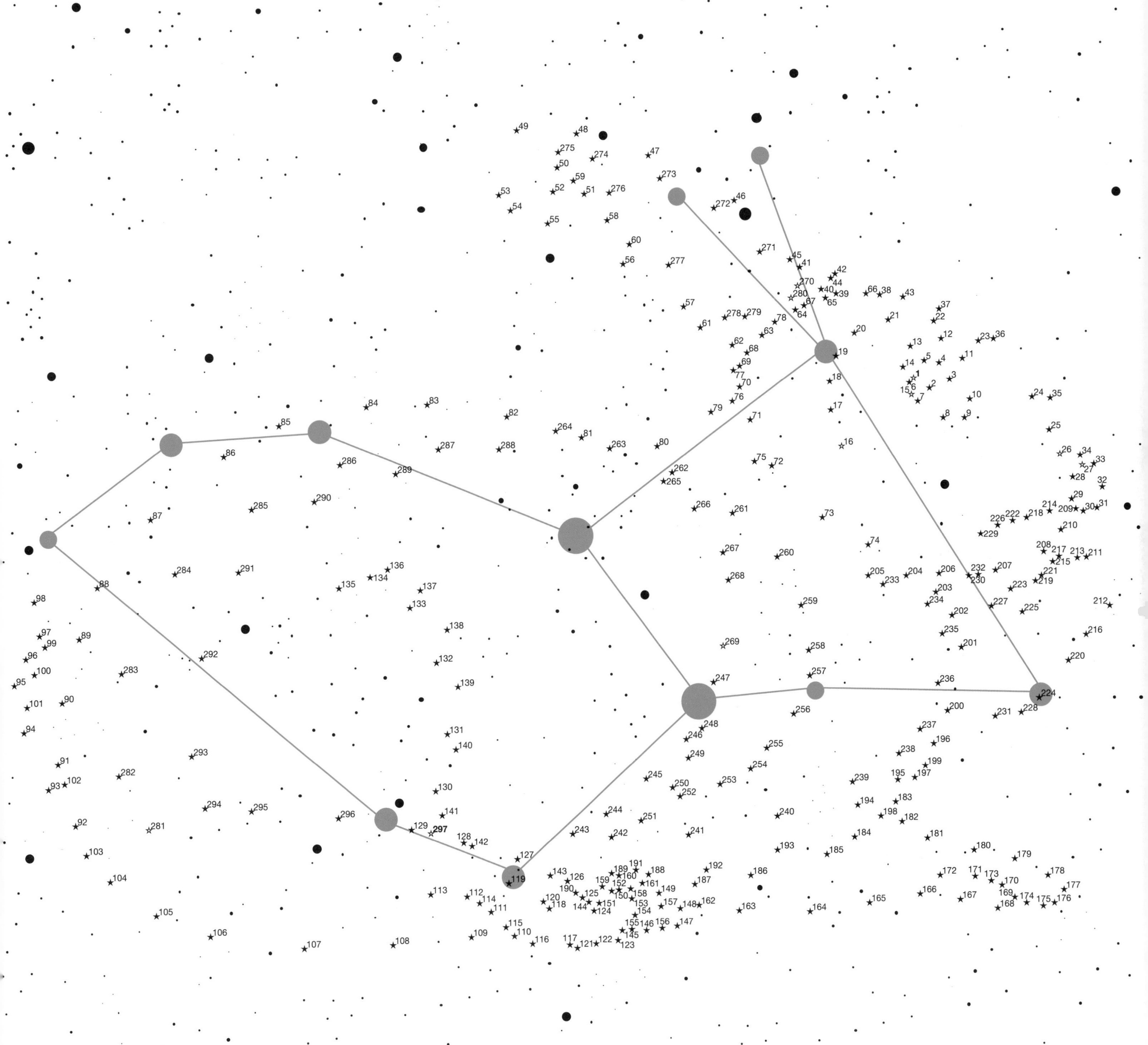

LUPUS

Not to be confused with Lepus (The Hare), Lupus means 'The Wolf' in Latin. It is a southern constellation lying between the figures of Centaurus and Scorpio in the sky. The ancient Greeks viewed Lupus as a wild animal being speared by a half-man, half-horse centaur.

LUPUS AT A GLANCE

What does its name mean?
'The Wolf' in Latin

Which is the brightest star?
Alpha Lupi

Where does this constellation lie?
In the Southern Hemisphere

To which constellation family does it belong?
Hercules

✱ IN MYTHOLOGY

To the ancient Greeks and Romans, Lupus was seen as part of the Centaurus constellation. A centaur attacked a wild animal, pierced it with a spear, and carried it to an altar as a sacrifice. In the sky, Centaurus holds Lupus towards the constellation Ara, which means 'altar'.

✱ AROUND THE WORLD

Various cultures referred to Lupus as a wild animal. It wasn't actually called a wolf until the 15th century.

- ur idim – 'wild dog-like creature' (Babylonia)
- therion – 'wild animal' (ancient Greece)
- bestia – 'beast' (ancient Rome)
- al sabu – 'wild beast' (Arab lands)

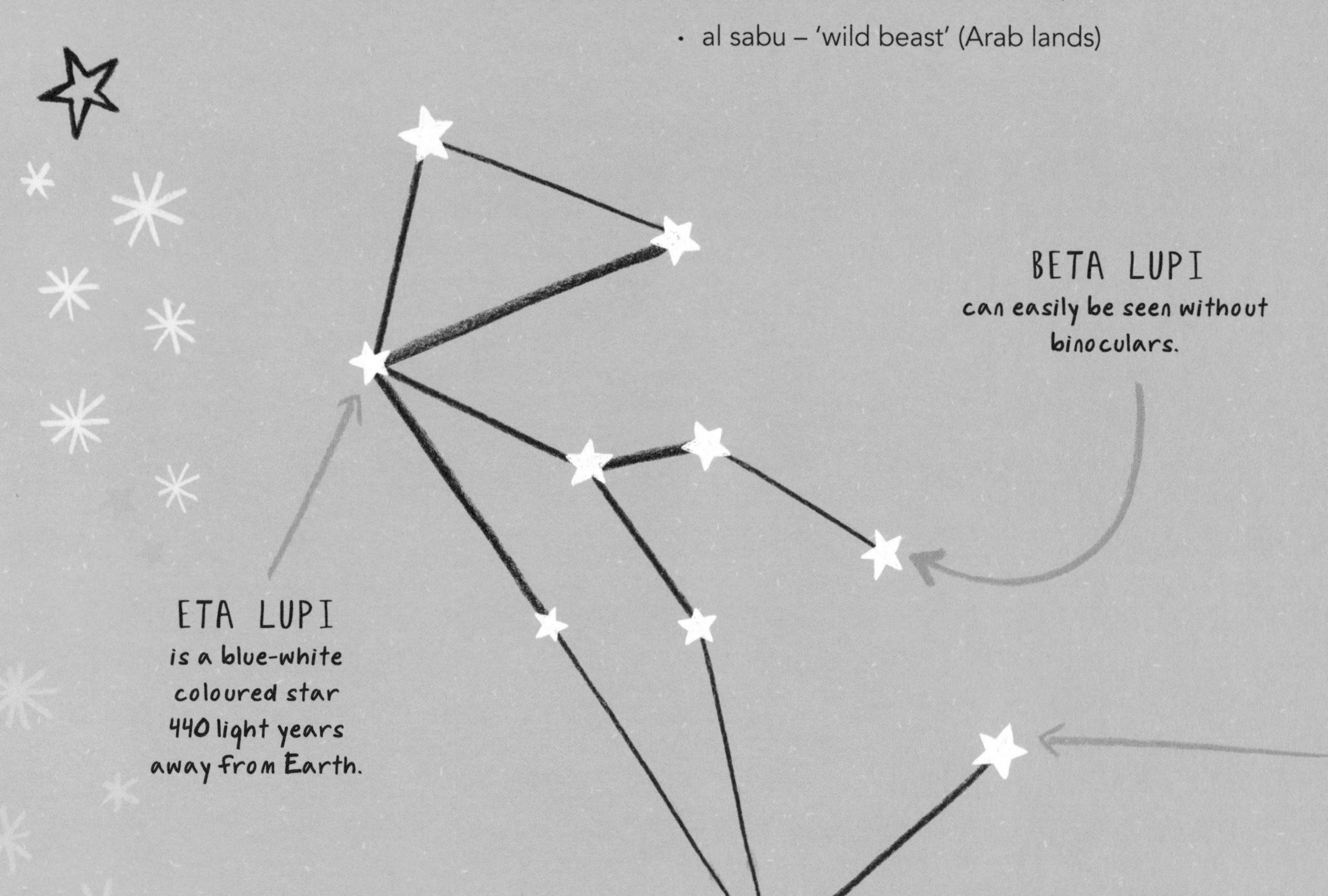
BETA LUPI
can easily be seen without binoculars.
ETA LUPI
is a blue-white coloured star 440 light years away from Earth.
ALPHA LUPI
is the brightest star in the Lupus constellation. It is 10 times the size of our Sun.

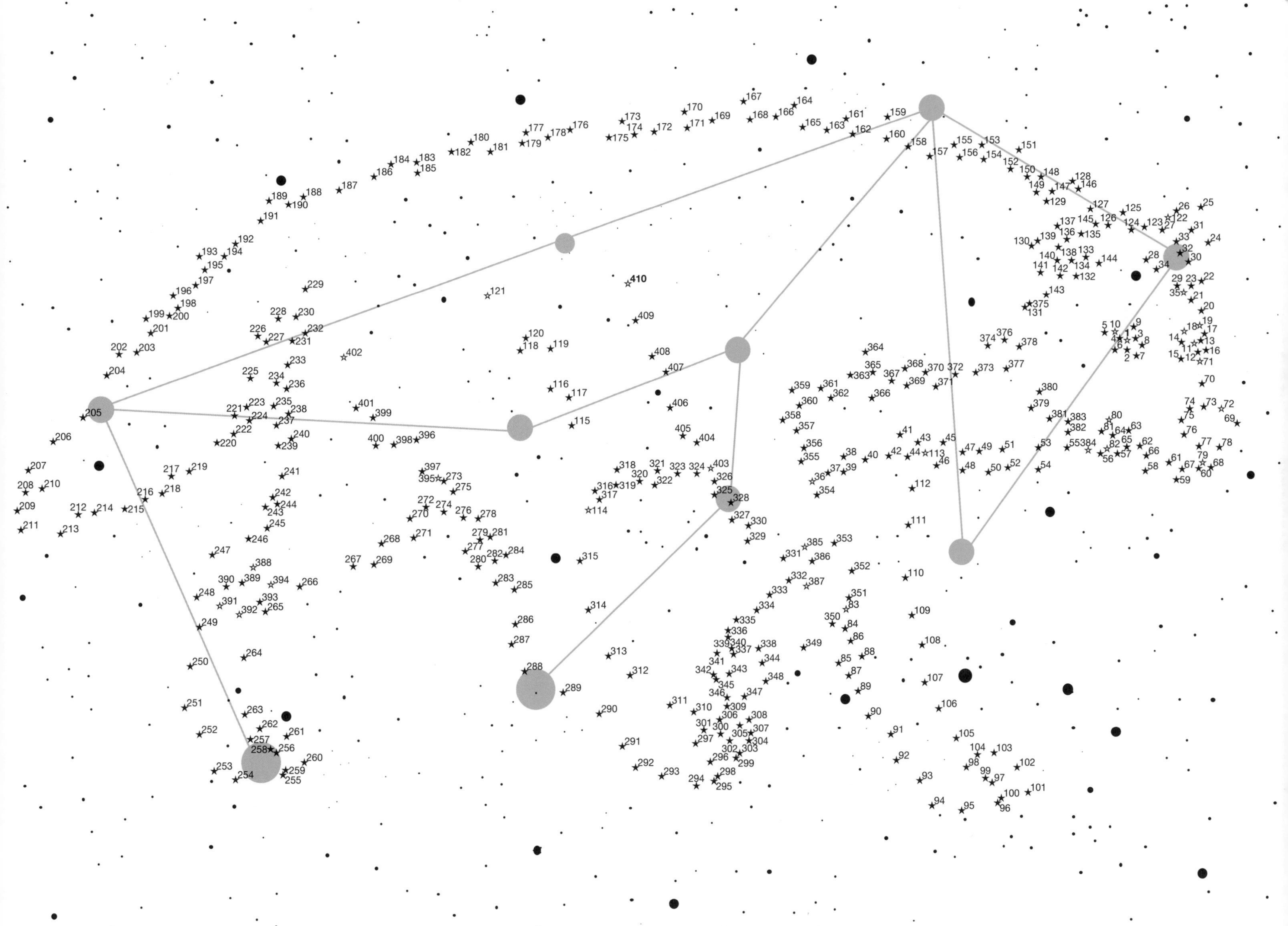

LYRA

Lyra might be small, but it makes up for its size in brightness! This constellation contains one of the sky's brightest stars, Vega, and is the subject of several Asian legends. Lyra represents 'The Lyre' (harp), belonging to the musician Orpheus, from Greek mythology.

LYRA AT A GLANCE

What does its name mean?
'The Lyre' or 'The Harp' in Latin

Which is the brightest star?
Vega (Alpha Lyrae)

Where does this constellation lie?
In the Northern Hemisphere

To which constellation family does it belong?
Hercules

* IN MYTHOLOGY

According to Asian legend, the star Vega was a beautiful goddess. She fell in love with a mortal man, represented by Altair, the brightest star in The Alquila (Eagle) constellation. The couple were forbidden to be together and ordered to stay on opposite sides of the river (the Milky Way). They can only unite on the seventh night of the seventh month of each year, when magpies (stars in the Cygnus constellation) form a bridge to bring the couple together.

* AROUND THE WORLD

Both instruments and animals are associated with Lyra:

- Harp (ancient Greece)
- King David's Harp (Wales)
- Tortoise (Arab lands)
- Falling vulture (ancient Egypt)

EPSILON LYRAE is a beautiful multiple star system†, one of the most famous in the whole sky.

SULAFAT (GAMMA LYRAE) is the second brightest star in the constellation. Its name means 'turtle' in Arabic, which refers to the shell used to make the body of the lyre.

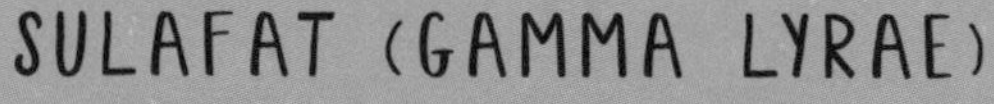

VEGA (ALPHA LYRAE) is Lyra's brightest star and the fifth brightest star in the sky. Its name comes from the Arabic word for 'swooping' because the star was seen by the Arabs as a swooping eagle.

STAR FACT

Vega forms part of the Summer Triangle, an asterism made up of the brightest stars from the Lyra, Cygnus and Aquila constellations.

SHEILAK (BETA LYRAE) is a binary star around 1,000 light years from Earth.

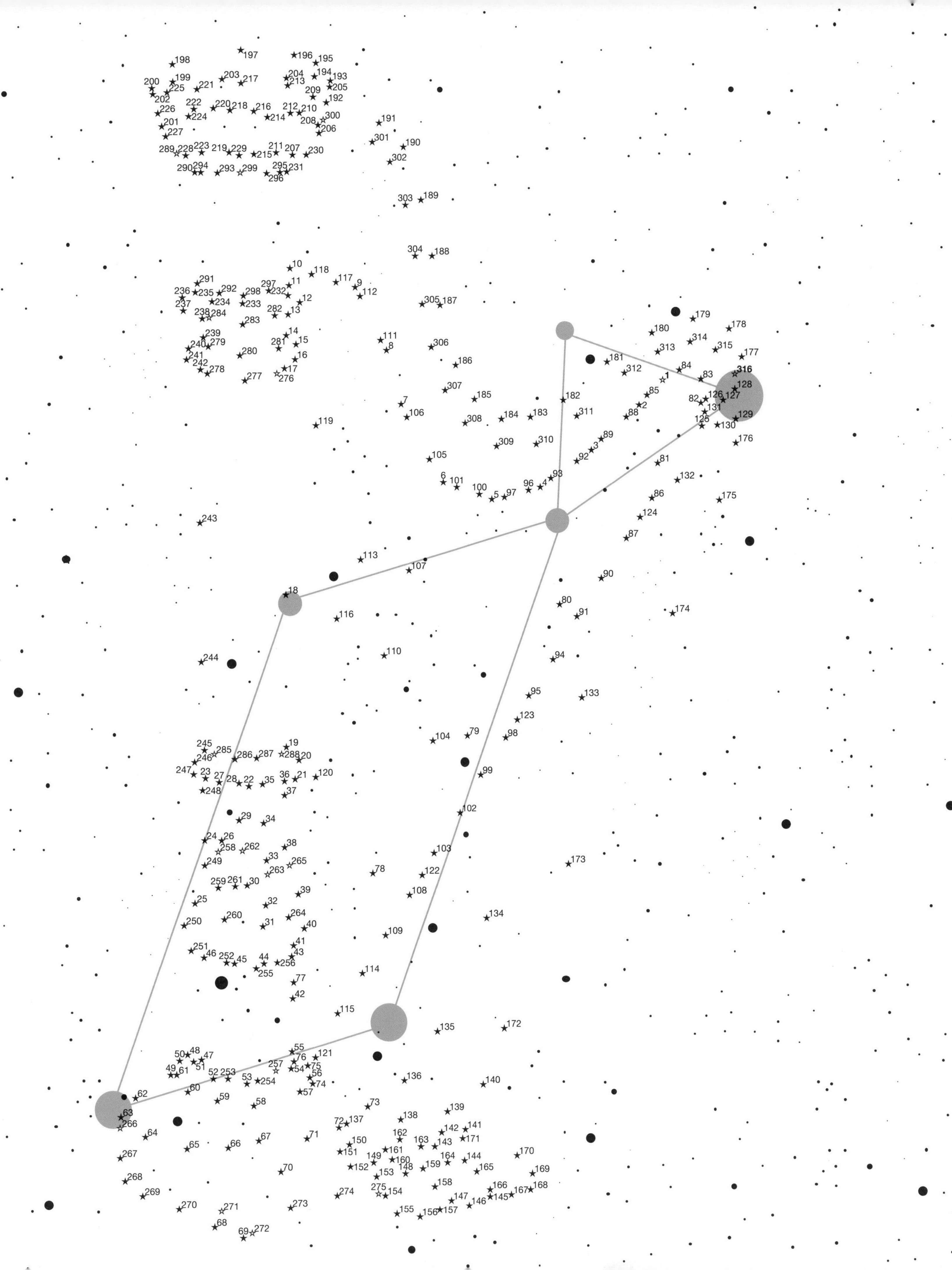

ANDROMEDA

This V-shaped constellation is named after the daughter of the mythical Queen Cassiopeia, seen in a nearby constellation. Andromeda's head is marked by its brightest star, Alpheratz, which also forms part of 'The Square of Pegasus' asterism.

ANDROMEDA AT A GLANCE

What does its name mean?
Name of a princess from Greek mythology

Which is the brightest star?
Alpheratz (Alpha Andromedae)

Where does this constellation lie?
In the Northern Hemisphere

To which constellation family does it belong?
Perseus

* IN MYTHOLOGY

As a result of her mother's vanity, Andromeda was chained to a rock and offered as a sacrifice to a fierce sea monster. The Greek hero, Perseus, swooped in to kill the monster and free Andromeda from her chains. The couple fell in love and were married. After her death, Andromeda was placed in the sky to join Perseus and her mother, Cassiopeia.

* AROUND THE WORLD

In Chinese astronomy, the stars in Andromeda join up with neighbouring stars to form different constellations. These represent a variety of things, such as:

- a person walking
- a palace wall
- a horse's stable
- a flying snake

THE ANDROMEDA GALAXY lies in Andromeda. It's the most distant object visible to the naked eye – 2.2 million light years away. It's on course to collide with our own galaxy, the Milky Way, in 5 billion years time.

ALMACH (GAMMA ANDROMEDAE) marks Andromeda's left foot. It is a multiple star system formed of four stars.

ALPHERATZ (ALPHA ANDROMEDAE) is sometimes known as Sirrah. Both names together mean 'horse's navel', because the star was once seen as part of the Pegasus constellation.

MIRACH (BETA ANDROMEDAE) is sometimes as bright as Alpheratz, but its brightness varies.

DRACO

With its twisting body, there's no mistaking that Draco represents a dragon-like creature. This is the dragon Ladon that was slain by Hercules (Heracles in the Greek tale). Nearby in the sky, Hercules stands with one triumphant foot on Draco's head.

DRACO AT A GLANCE

What does its name mean?
'The Dragon' in Latin

Which is the brightest star?
Etamin (Gamma Draconis)

Where does this constellation lie?
In the Northern Hemisphere

To which constellation family does it belong?
Ursa Major

* IN MYTHOLOGY

The best-known story tells of Ladon, dragon guardian of the Garden of Hersperides, who was killed by Hercules, the strong and fearless hero. In Roman myth, Draco was one of the Gigantes – giants who fought for many years against the gods. The dragon was killed by the goddess of wisdom, Minerva, who threw it to the stars, where it froze in its twisted form forever.

* AROUND THE WORLD

In Arabic astronomy, Draco's stars are seen as a group of mother camels forming a protective ring around a baby camel, who is being attacked by hyenas.

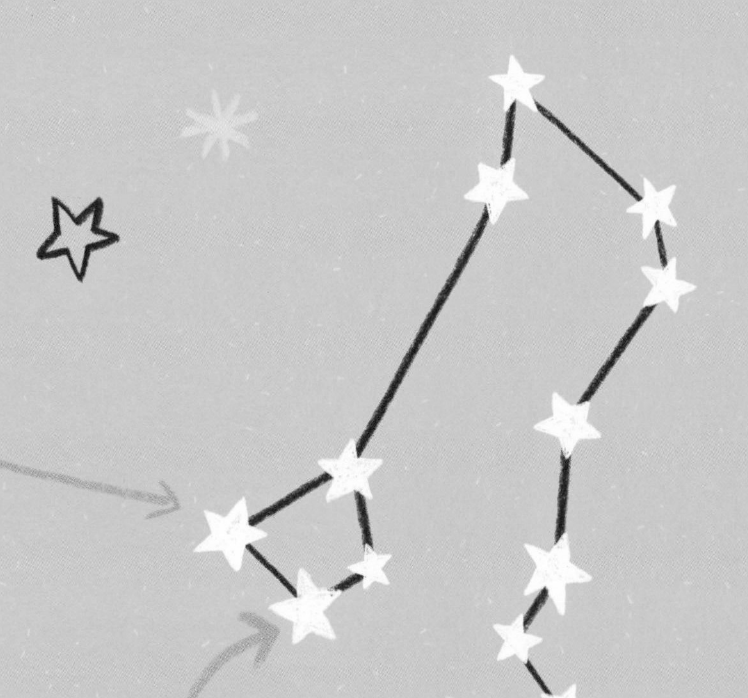

ETAMIN (GAMMA DRACONIS) is Draco's brightest star. In about 1.5 million years, it will pass within 28 light years of Earth and will take Sirius' place as the brightest star in our sky.

THUBAN (ALPHA DRACONIS) Thousands of years ago, this was once the North Star – the closest star to the North Pole. (This is now Polaris.)

STAR FACT

Draco contains the beautiful Cat's Eye nebula, layers of gases glowing around a dying star, which is 3,000 light years from Earth.

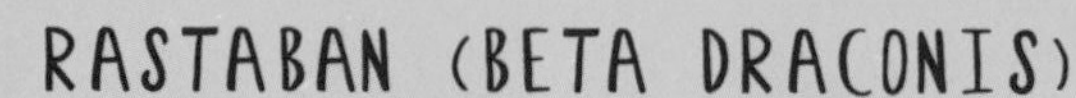

forms part of the dragon's head. Its name comes from the Arabic word for 'head of the serpent'.

CRATER

Crater, which means 'The Cup' in Latin, is a small, faint constellation in the Southern Hemisphere, near Hydra (The Water Snake) and Corvus (The Crow). Crater represents the cup of the Greek god Apollo.

CRATER AT A GLANCE

What does its name mean?
'The Cup' in Latin

Which is the brightest star?
Labrum (Delta Crateris)

Where does this constellation lie?
In the Southern Celestial Hemisphere, but is visible in the Northern Hemisphere for a short time.

To which constellation family does it belong?
Hercules

* IN MYTHOLOGY

Apollo, the sun god, sent his pet crow to fetch water in his cup. On its way, the crow stopped by a fig tree to rest and feast on the fruits. When the crow finally arrived back with the filled cup for Apollo, it also brought with it a water snake. The crow made up a lie that he had been attacked by the snake, and this was why he was so late. Angry at the lies, Apollo sent the crow, the snake and the cup into the sky, where the snake (as Hydra) guards the cup of water from the thirsty crow.

* AROUND THE WORLD

Other cultures through history also viewed Crater as a kind of cup:

- Vessel for storing wine (Arab lands)
- Container for ashes (ancient Greece)
- Cup of Bacchus, Roman god of wine (ancient Rome)
- Two-handed pot (English)

LABRUM (DELTA CRATERIS) is an orange giant star, and the brightest in the constellation. Its name is Latin for 'lip'.

ALKES (ALPHA CRATERIS) means 'the cup' in Arabic.

GAMMA CRATERIS is located at the centre of the cup and is Crater's second brightest star.

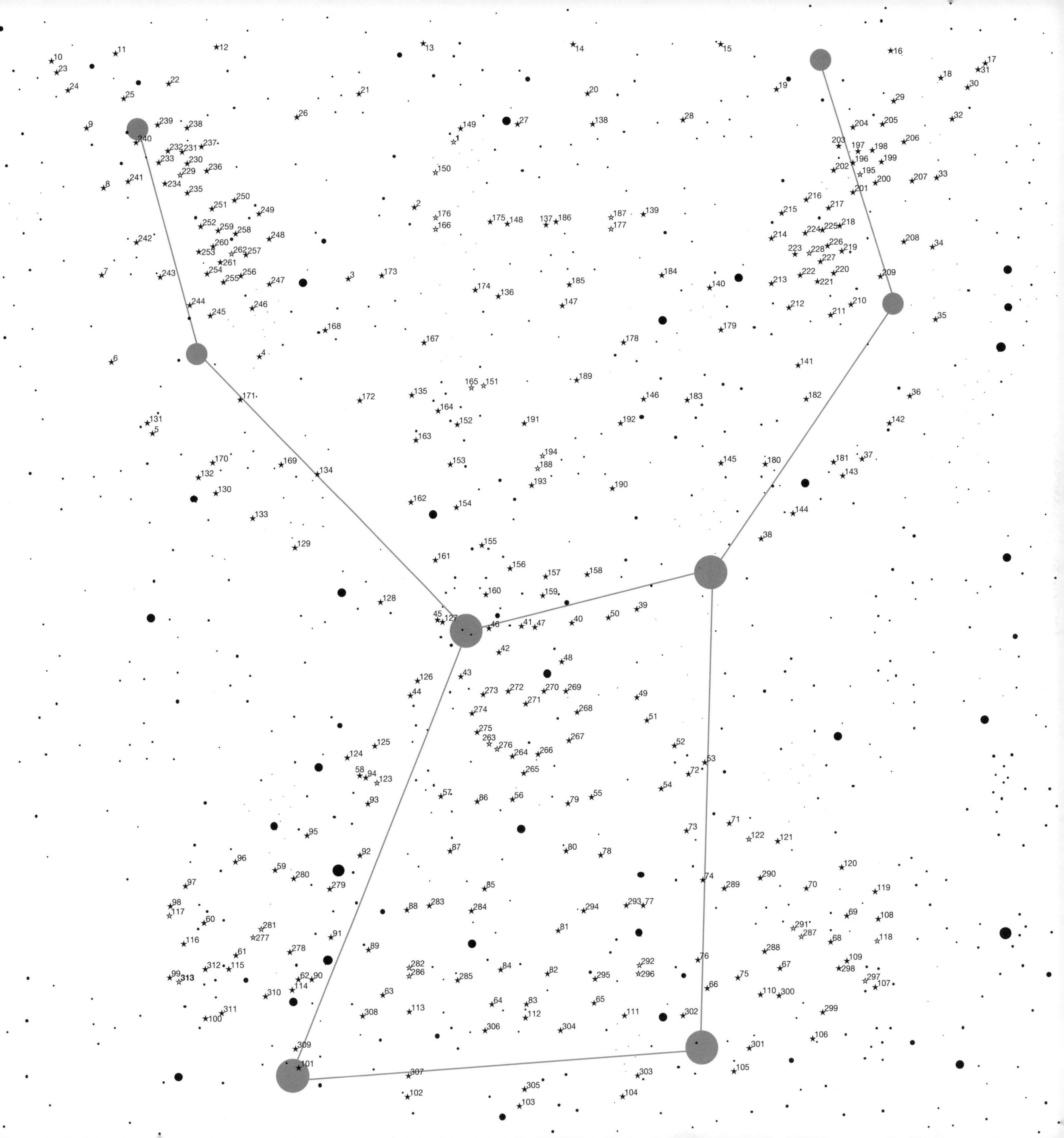

DELPHINUS

Small but easy to recognize, Delphinus, 'The Dolphin', glides across the northern sky on late summer nights. Four stars outline its body, with the fifth forming its tail. Delphinus is usually associated with the Greek story of Poseidon, the sea god, and Amphitrite, the nymph.

DELPHINUS AT A GLANCE

What does its name mean?
'The Dolphin' in Latin

Which is the brightest star?
Sualocin (Alpha Delphini)

Where does this constellation lie?
In the Northern Hemisphere

To which constellation family does it belong?
Heavenly Waters

* IN MYTHOLOGY

Poseidon, Greek god of the sea, was in love with the nymph Amphitrite, but she did not love him back. To try and win her affections, Poseidon sent a group of messengers to find her and bring her to him. The dolphin was one of these messengers. It found Amphritite, and managed to convince her to love and marry Poseidon. To thank the dolphin, Poseidon placed it among the stars.

* AROUND THE WORLD

The Delphinus constellation has been seen as:

- a gourd (fruit) (China)
- a bird cage (India)
- a trumpet shell (Aboriginal Australia)
- a riding camel (Arab lands)

SUALOCIN (ALPHA DELPHINI) is named after 19th-century Italian astronomer Niccolo Cacciatore. 'Sualocin' is the Latin version of his first name, spelled backwards. It is the brightest star in Delphinus.

DENEB DULFIM (EPSILON DELPHINI) marks the dolphin's tail, the meaning of its name in Arabic.

ROTANEV (BETA DELPHINI) is the second brightest star. Like Sualocin, it is named after Niccolo Cacciatore. His surname means 'hunter' in Italian. 'Rotanev' spelled backwards is Venator, which, in Latin, also means 'hunter'.

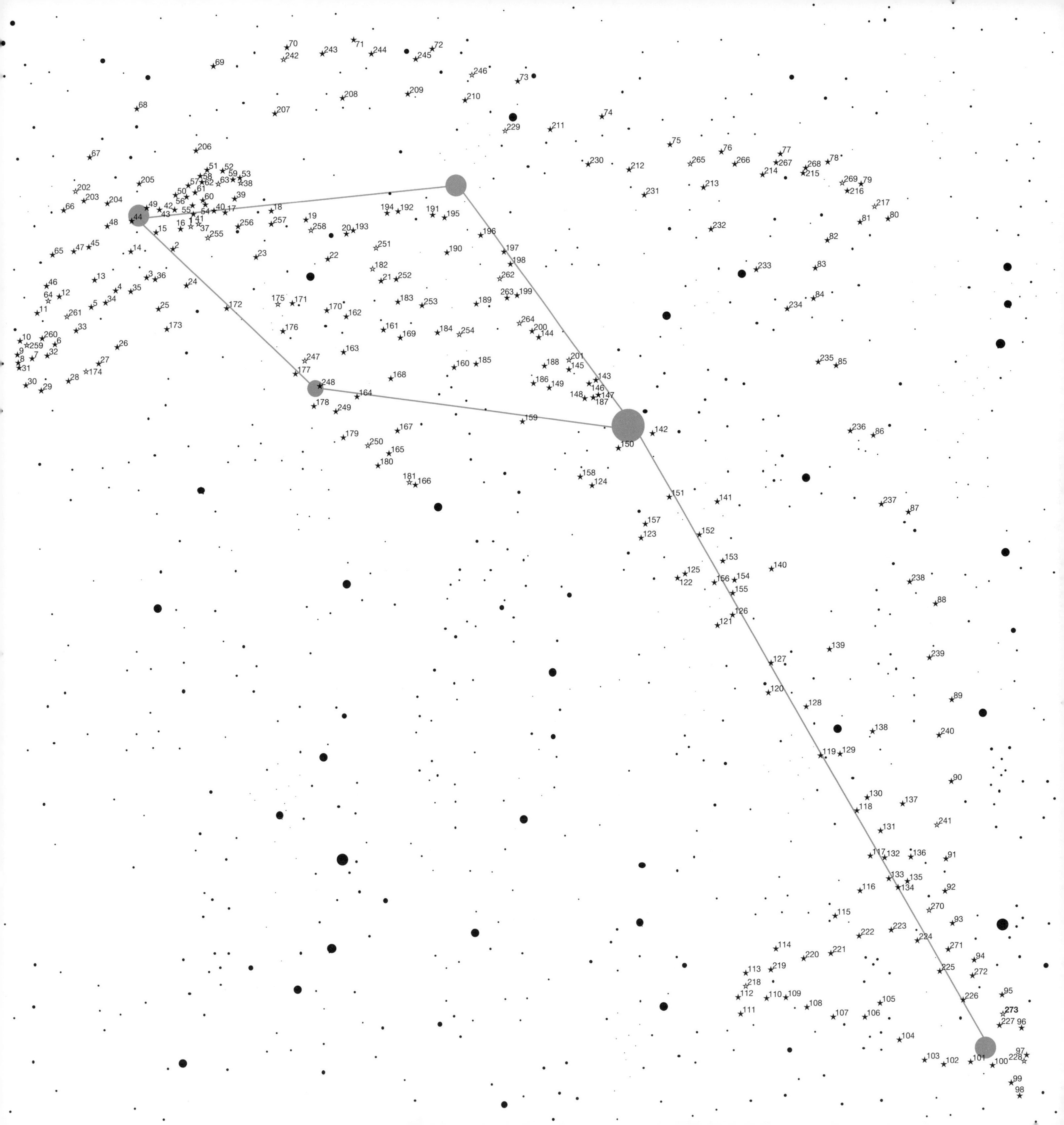

HYDRA

Snaking its way over a quarter of the sky is Hydra, the sea serpent. The largest of all 88 constellations, Hydra shares its name with the multi-headed monster from Greek mythology that battled Hercules in his Second Labour. A group of five stars marks Hydra's head.

* IN MYTHOLOGY

The Hydra was a fearsome monster with nine heads, one of which was immortal. As part of his Second Labour, Hercules was sent to kill the monster and cut off all its heads. Battling the Hydra with the help of his assistant, he managed to burn off its heads and bury the last, immortal head under a rock.

* AROUND THE WORLD

In Chinese astronomy, Hydra's head forms part of the head of the Vermilion (Red) Bird.

In Hindu astronomy, Hydra is also associated with a snake-like creature. It is known as the 'Clinging Star' or 'Entwiner' (which refers to the way the snake winds itself around its prey).

HYDRA AT A GLANCE

What does its name mean?
'The Water Snake' in Latin

Which is the brightest star?
Alphard (Alpha Hydrae)

Where does this constellation lie?
In the Southern Hemisphere

To which constellation family does it belong?
Hercules

STAR FACT

Hydra is such a large constellation that it takes six hours to rise and become fully visible in the night sky – longer than any other constellation.

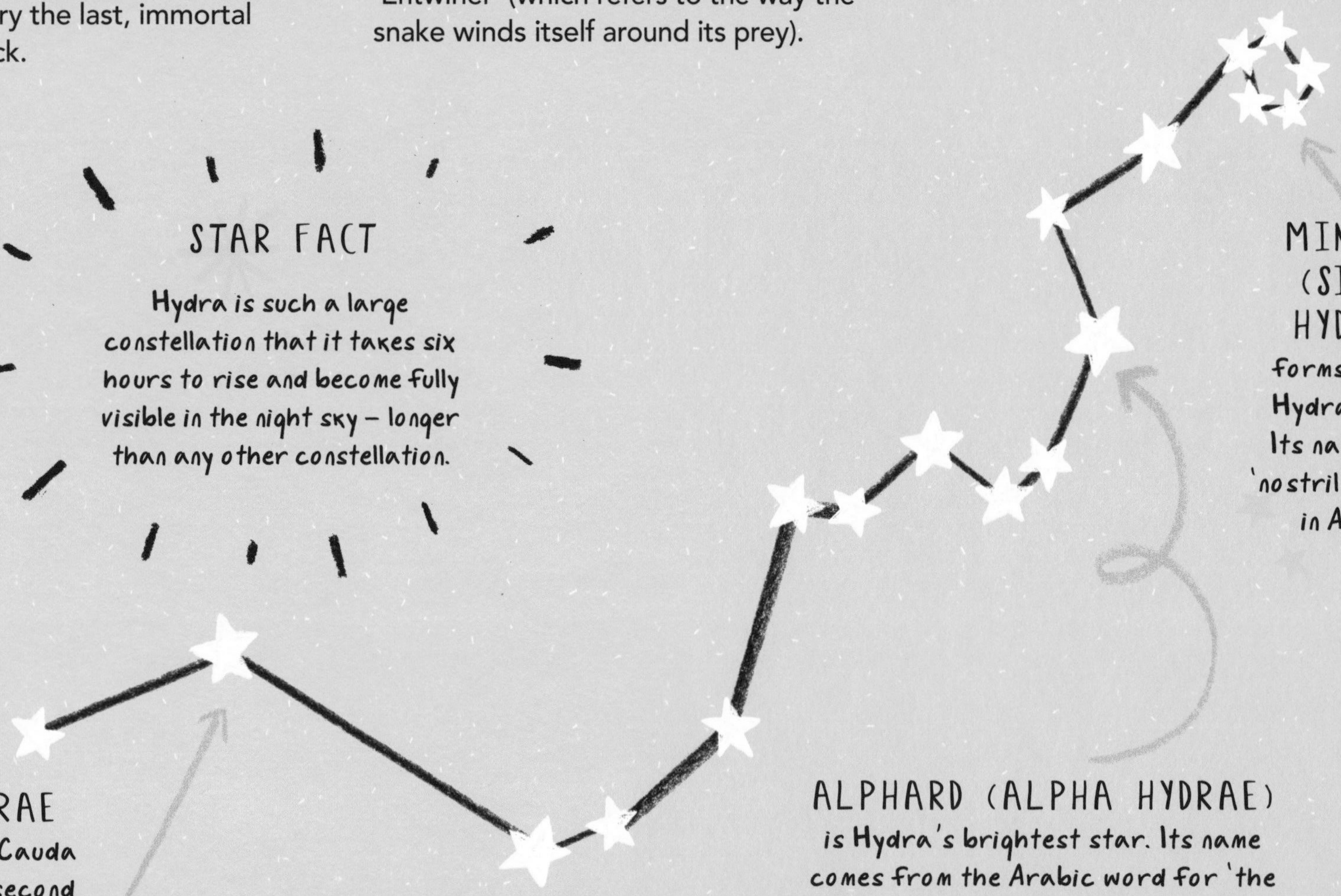

MINCHIR (SIGMA HYDRAE) forms part of Hydra's head. Its name means 'nostril of Hydra' in Arabic.

GAMMA HYDRAE
Sometimes called 'Cauda Hydrae', it is the second brightest star. Its age is around 372 million years, which is much younger than our Sun of 4.5 billion years.

ALPHARD (ALPHA HYDRAE) is Hydra's brightest star. Its name comes from the Arabic word for 'the solitary one', as there are not many other stars around it.

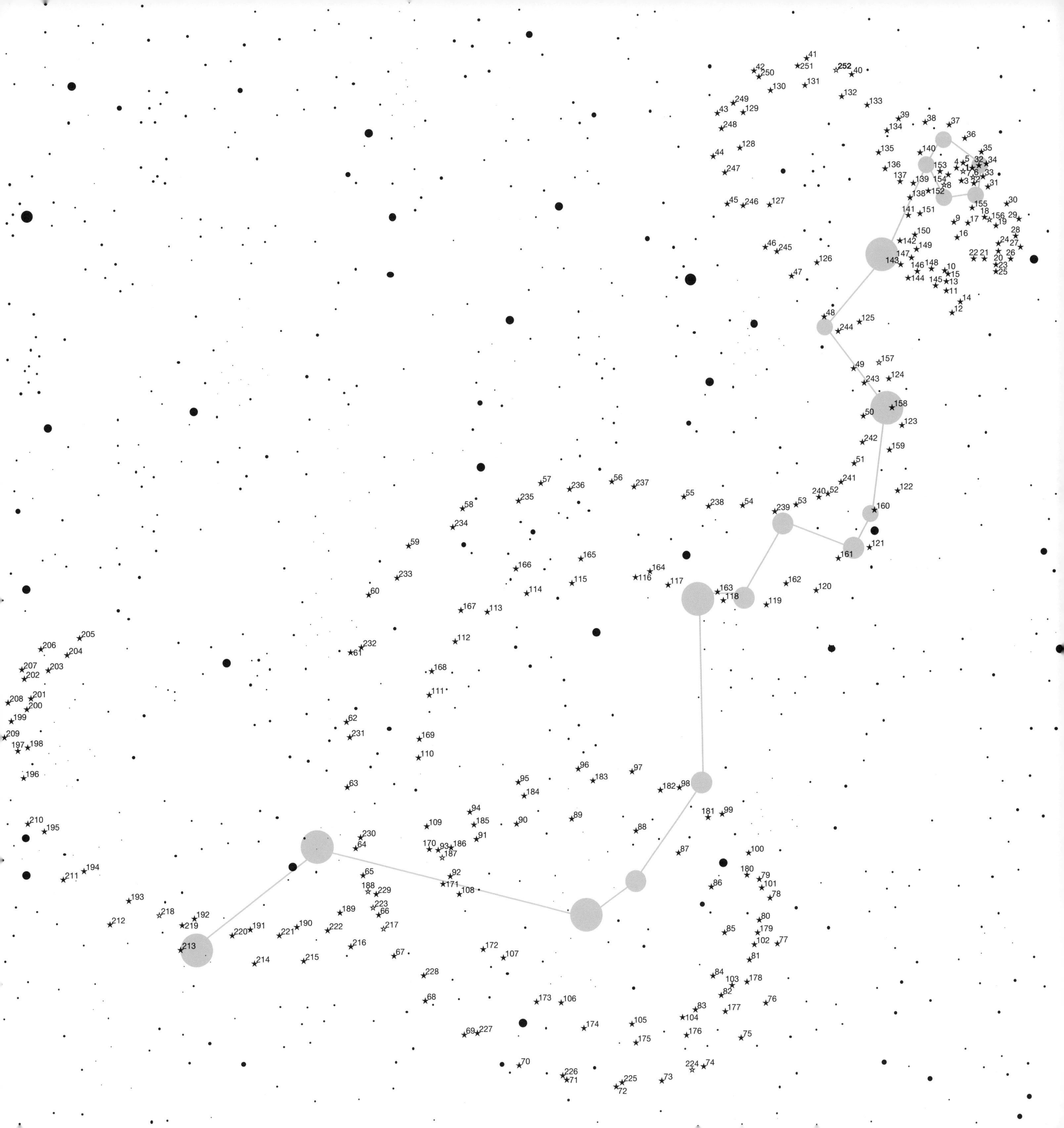

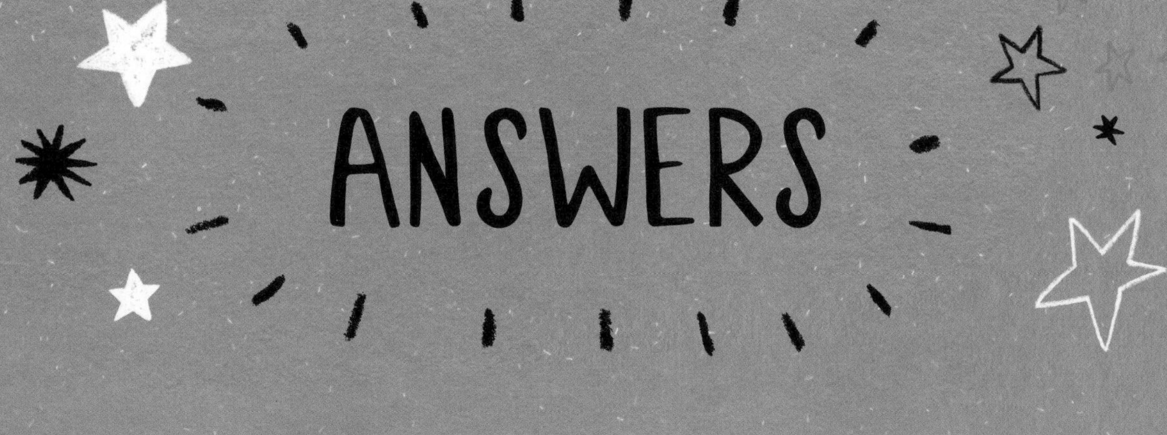

ANSWERS

PISCES

CAPRICORNUS

TAURUS

AQUARIUS

ARIES

GEMINI

CANIS MAJOR

CORONA BOREALIS

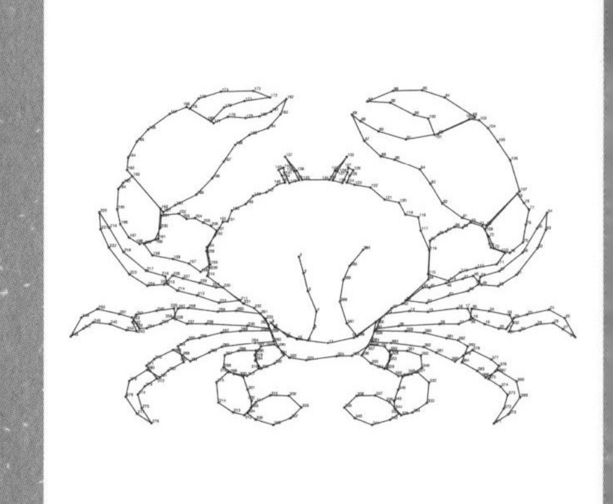

CANCER

LEO

VIRGO

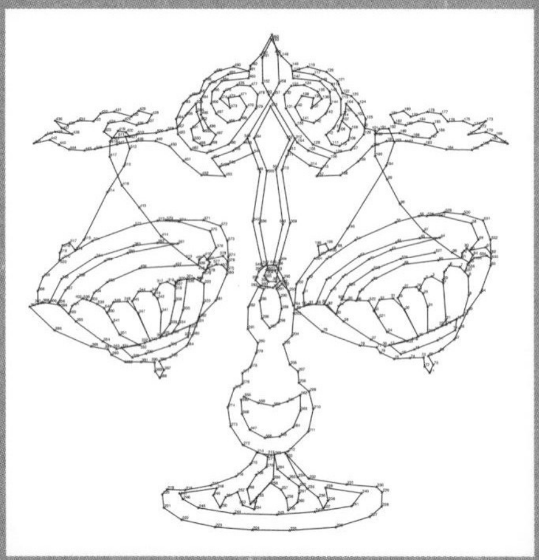

LIBRA

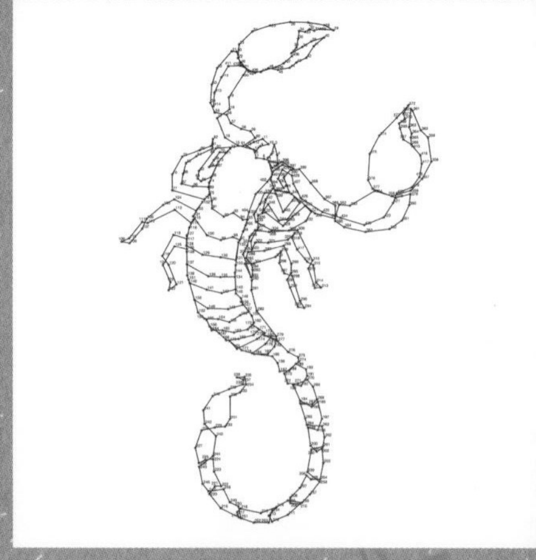

SCORPIUS

SAGITTARIUS
CYGNUS
ORION
URSA MAJOR
PEGASUS
CASSIOPEIA
CRUX
HERCULES
LEPUS
LUPUS
LYRA
ANDROMEDA
DRACO
CRATER
DELPHINUS
HYDRA

GLOSSARY

asterism: a pattern of stars recognized in the sky. It may be part of a constellation or it may be made up of stars from more than one constellation.

BCE / CE: Before Common Era / Common Era, sometimes expressed as BC and AD.

binary star: a star system containing two stars that orbit around the same centre.

Celestial Hemisphere: an imaginary sphere surrounding the Earth.

double star: a pair of stars that appear close to each other as seen from Earth, but which actually lie at different distances.

exoplanet: a planet that orbits a star outside our own Solar System.

globular star cluster: a collection of stars that are tightly bound by gravity, which gives them their spherical shape.

gravity: a natural phenomenon by which all things with mass are brought towards one another, including planets, stars and galaxies.

hemisphere: each half of the Earth's sphere, divided by the equator into the Northern and Southern Hemispheres.

latitude: a series of imaginary circles drawn around the Earth parallel to the equator.

light year: a unit of distance equivalent to the distance that light travels in one year.

Milky Way: the galaxy that contains our Solar System. Its name derives from its appearance as a milky band arching across the night sky.

multiple star system: a group of three or more stars bound to each other by gravity†.

nebula: a cloud of gas and dust in outer space, visible in the night sky either as an indistinct bright patch or as a dark silhouette.

open star cluster: a group of stars that were formed from the same cloud and that are still loosely bound to each other by gravity.

orbit: the gravitationally curved path of an object about a point in space, for example the orbit of a planet about a star or a moon around a planet.

solstice: an astronomical event that occurs twice each year (in June and December) as the Sun reaches its nearest and furthest distance from the equator.

supergiant star: the most massive and brightest stars in the universe. They can have a mass up to 100 times greater than our Sun.

supernova: an explosion of a massive supergiant star.

First published in Great Britain in 2017 by Michael O'Mara Books Limited,
9 Lion Yard, Tremadoc Road, London SW4 7NQ

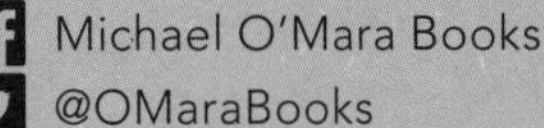
www.mombooks.com
Michael O'Mara Books
@OMaraBooks

www.drgarethmoore.com

Contains material adapted from www.shutterstock.com

A CIP catalogue record for this book is available from the British Library.

ISBN: 978-1-78243-731-4

1 3 5 7 9 10 8 6 4 2

This book was printed in China.